Man marks the earth with ruin . . .
"Are we perhaps fated to mark the ocean with ruin, to plunder, pollute, and contend until we have a ghost ocean bereft of all but the voice of its waves?"

Written with great vividness and power and out of deep concern, THE FRAIL OCEAN gives harrowing examples of Man's marking the sea with ruin—the specters of a savaged kelp forest off the southern California coast; the burial of the estuaries, nature's rich nurseries, by ill-conceived land reclamation projects; dumping of radioactive wastes which are now being detected in marine life; and the *Torrey Canyon* disaster of March, 1967 which spilled 36,000,000 gallons of crude oil into England's offshore, blighting the region's wildlife and threatening its tourist economy—all give grim testimony to the savage destruction of our most precious resource.

Impassioned in his indictment of Man's ruthless exploitation of the seas, Wesley Marx also writes with lyric joy, reminiscent of Rachel Carson's, of the ocean's splendor, communicating his sense of wonder at its enormous power and fertility, as well as his growing fear for its future.

THE FRAIL OCEAN makes an eloquent plea—a plea that grows more urgent with each new ocean disaster—for the preservation of the seas and their myriad inhabitants—before it is too late.

The Frail Ocean

Wesley Marx

BALLANTINE BOOKS • NEW YORK

Acknowledgments

I gratefully acknowledge the many people who helped me to prepare this book. Dr. Wheeler North of the California Institute of Technology provided valuable and personal knowledge of the sea forests of California. He also reviewed a draft of the chapter on sea forests. Dr. Theodore Walker of Scripps Institution of Oceanography allowed me to join him on a memorable excursion to Scammon Lagoon to observe the gray whales. Dr. Carl Hubbs, also of Scripps, and his wife shared their experiences at the lagoon with me one afternoon.

Mr. A. C. Rayner of the U.S. Army Coastal Engineering Research Center in Washington forwarded some very helpful material on beach erosion, and members of the Los Angeles office of the Corps of Engineers also cooperated in supplying related reports.

Dr. Claude ZoBell of Scripps and Dr. Nuri Malley of Space-General Corporation enlightened me on the subject of oil pollution.

Dr. John Kask, director of the Inter-American Tropical Tuna Commission, helped acquaint me with the fascinating tropical tuna fishery. Dr. Kask also reviewed the chapter on this subject. Mr. Witold Klawe of the Commission provided me with some very helpful material on the Eastern Tropical Pacific. Mr. Klawe and Mr. Thomas Calkins of the Commission reviewed the chapter on this subject for scientific and technical accuracy. Mr. Gerald Howard, director, Pacific Southwest Region, Bureau of Commercial Fisheries and Theodore Green of the Bureau of Commercial Fisheries Biological Laboratory at La Jolla introduced me to the techniques of tuna capture, present and future. Mr. August Felando, general manager of the American Tunaboat Association, very kindly initiated me into the economic and political problems of the tuna fishery.

Mr. Arch Ekdale, Proctor in Admiralty, San Pedro, California, provided some valuable insights into the evolving law of the sea, and Mrs. Donald McLaughlin, secretary of the Save San Francisco Bay Association, supplied helpful material on the condition of the bay.

From overseas, Dr. Makio Uchida of the Kumamoto University Medical School forwarded valuable information on the Minamata-disease investigation, Dr. H. Postma of the Netherlands Institute for Sea Research shared the results of his investigations into the oceanography of Scammon Lagoon, and Dr. Enrique Beltran, director of the Mexican Institute of Renewable Natural Resources, supplied information on possible efforts to preserve the lagoon.

Mr. Thomas Tugend, public information officer with the School of Engineering at the University of California at Los Angeles, permitted me to monitor a course on oceanography developments. The Information Office of Submarine Flotilla Number One arranged a tour of the USS *Razorback*.

Mr. Robert Manning, editor of the *Atlantic Monthly*, provided a large dose of encouragement by publishing two of my initial articles on the ocean.

My father kindly read portions of this manuscript and made helpful comments. My wife did the same and also chipped in with admirable displays of patience amid writing deadlines.

Any author who purports to discuss the ocean is indebted to a woman who contributed so gracefully to its public appreciation—Miss Rachel Carson.

WESLEY MARX

Irvine, California
December 29, 1966

Contents

The Frail Ocean

1.

The Obsolete Ocean

RECENTLY I roamed through a dying forest. The blades of bulldozers and the teeth of power saws accomplish such destruction rather routinely today, though neither bulldozers nor humming power saws killed this particular forest. No towns or farms or log runs emerged to give meaning to its vanishing, for it lay deep within the sea. Huge seaweed plants called giant kelp once formed a lush foliage that sheltered life as profuse and vital as that of any land forest. Today the forest is no more. No leafy canopy sprawls over the sea surface to shaft the marine sun and shadow schools of fish. Instead the sun pours in, spotlighting an occasional survivor of this underwater devastation—a stray bass.

The disappearance of this sea forest is linked to a relatively new element in the ocean's makeup: man. Scientists now feel that the forest was subverted by the surprisingly subtle effects of a sewage outfall, jutting out from the coast of southern California.

It may be difficult to accept the fact that our progress can mean death to the ocean. Although the land has long been a sweating resource, the ocean has always been considered an impenetrable redoubt of nature, impervious to man's acquisitiveness and his carelessness alike. We celebrate its omnipotence in verse, in music, and in art. George Gordon, Lord Byron, who loved to body surf in the North Sea, wrote of the joys of the "society where none intrudes" and wondered at its power:

> Roll on, thou deep and dark blue ocean—roll!
> Ten thousand fleets sweep over thee in vain;
> Man marks the earth with ruin—his control
> Stops with the shore.

The ocean stirred Melville, Conrad, Stevenson, and many of our most distinguished writers to their finest achievements. Even the simple beauty of an ocean marsh was enough to inspire Sidney Lanier:

> Oh, what is abroad in the marsh and the terminal sea?
> Somehow my soul seems suddenly free
> From the weighing of fate and the sad discussion of sin.

And, over the years, it has been equally inspiring to musicians and artists. Claude Debussy's best known work is a hymn to the sea. Winslow Homer, a fledgling artist in search of a subject, began painting the ocean off the New Jersey shore. Then he moved north, set up a portable painting booth on the surf-dashed cliffs of Maine, and donned oilskins to paint during savage storms. For the last twenty-seven years of his life Homer, the semirecluse, painted the sea in all its moods. Today his work is admired in museums throughout the United States.

No other natural phenomenon on this planet—not even mountains five miles high, rivers spilling over cliffs, or redwood forests—evokes such reverence. Yet this same "all-powerful" ocean now proves as slavishly subservient to natural laws as a moth caught by candlelight or a rose seed blown into the Atlantic. The ocean obeys. It heeds. It complies. It has its tolerances and its stresses. When these are surpassed, the ocean falters. Fish stocks can be depleted. The nurseries of marine life can be buried.

Beaches can erode away. Seawater, the most common substance on this earth and the most life-nourishing—at once liquid soil and liquid atmosphere—can be hideously corrupted. It can host substances that in the stomachs of oysters or clams are refined into poisons that paralyze porpoise and man alike.

Or as it became appallingly clear on March 18, 1967, an entire ocean region can suddenly find itself in direct jeopardy. The Atlantic Ocean off the southern tip of Great Britain sparkled deep blue, unsullied by running whitecaps or shadowing storm clouds. Guillemots, auks, redshanks, herons, and Panzance fishermen dipped into this blue world, drawing succor from its life-giving energy. At Land's End, hotel owners ordered new carpets to greet London's annual summer pilgrimage to the Cornish coast. Since the sapping of its tin mines and fertile lands, the magnet of ocean beaches alone keeps Cornwall from sinking into economic depression.

As the world discovered, the spilled cargo of one ship twenty miles away managed to shatter this serenity as no gale could do. The cargo of the reef-gashed *Torrey Canyon* was a liquid one, totaling thirty-six million gallons, ordinarily a raindrop in the vast solution of the ocean. But the ocean cannot absorb oil very efficiently. Within three days, slicks the color of melted chocolate sprawled over one hundred square miles of ocean, a moving quagmire that ensnared seabirds by the thousands. The slicks, with their chirping cargo of flightless birds, rolled up on the golden beaches of Cornwall. Land's End smelled like an oil refinery. Like the oil-fouled birds, the oysters, clams, and teeming inhabitants of tidepools found themselves encased in a straightjacket of Kuwait crude. Three weeks later and some two hundred miles away, the pink granite coast of Brittany received the same greasy absolution from *la marée noire*. Silently, without the fanfare of howling winds and crashing waves, this oil-stricken ocean was coating the coastlines of two countries with havoc.

Great Britain, perhaps history's most famous maritime nation, swiftly mobilized its forces. RAF jets dropped napalm bombs on the slicks to fire them into oblivion. It was like a grand military campaign. (JENKINS TELLS OF PLAN TO USE THE VIETNAM HORROR BOMB, proclaimed an extra edition of the London *Daily Mirror*.) But the open ocean, heeding its own laws, dispersed the spilled oil into a slick solution that—the reporter on the scene for the *Economist* noted—is "incombustible by anything short of the fires of hell." From napalm bombs, the campaign accelerated to include a fleet of thirty warships armed with chemical detergents. Yet the detergent fleet could hardly cope with the extent of the slicks, and those that they did manage to emulsify drifted down into the ocean depths to asphyxiate schools of fish. Great Britain retreated to its shores, and Tommies, along with children using garden spray cans, began deploying detergent on the beaches. Ironically, the detergent created a milky liquid more toxic to shellfish than Kuwait crude, and much of the muck had then to be shoveled up. Meanwhile, in makeshift hospitals, bird lovers, their hands clawed red, cleaned terrified oil-smeared seabirds with talcum. The nation that started out to napalm the fireproof sea was hand-cleansing its beaches and its birds—and waiting for the next high tide. The British Prime Minister, who had called out the RAF, tried to cheer up Cornwall's worried hotel and shop owners, their livelihood suddenly threatened. "I am not canceling my holiday in that part of the world," said Harold Wilson reassuringly. Some hotelkeepers canceled their carpet orders; others rolled up their carpets, while one more inventive owner prohibited the wearing of shoes in his hotel. When oil from a Liberian tanker grounded in international waters and controlled by an American company smears your rugs, whom do you sue? Today marine bacteria, the only creatures that can stomach Kuwait crude, busily feast on the remains of the slicks.

Unlike a roaring tidal wave, this oil-tortured ocean overturned no ships, leveled no houses, and took no lives. Yet as no single wave could do, it endangered the coastal resources of two nations and compelled the English government to spend more than three and a half million dollars to forestall its stealthy but inexorable invasion. There are now plans to make it easier to sue shipowners, to adapt a flight control system to crowded coastal navigation, and to empower nations to perform instant "explosive surgery" on injured ships with potential oil slicks sloshing inside their hulls. Proposals are also under consideration to dynamite coastal reefs and similar navigational hazards.

Yet despite a clear day, calm waters, high tide, excellent charts, a warning flare from a lighthouse ship and a sterling 100A1 rating from Lloyd's Insurers, the *Torrey Canyon* still slammed into Seven Stones Reef to become a historic shipwreck. Only one natural phenomenon can overcome so many safeguards. Negligence was the charge laid down against the *Torrey Canyon*'s captain by a Liberian board of inquiry. With the ocean being impressed into duty as a giant oil conduit, there will be more inevitable oil leaks and oil spills, whether off Cape Cod, in the Baltic or Mediterranean seas, or off Los Angeles Harbor, where the *Torrey Canyon* grounded once before —on a shoal of soft sand. There will also be a new style of oil spill—the offshore oil blowout that can coat 800 square miles of nearshore and smear 30 miles of beach, as happened in the Union Oil blowout off Santa Barbara, Ca., in 1969. We are becoming the demanding taskmaster of the ocean, yet the ocean is endowed with stresses and limits that cannot always tolerate our ambitions or our errors.

The stresses on the ocean are ceaselessly intensifying. As land resources shrink, the world's population and its expectations expand. Indeed, the functions of land on a congested planet that consists largely of water may narrow to one: providing living space for man. Already we contend with orange groves and cattle ranches for elbow room. The continuing depletion and/or usurpation of land resources raises the need for a new storehouse of energy to keep the Technological Revolution fueled with food, water, pharmaceuticals, gas, and minerals. Barring cultivation of the universe, the ocean emerges as that vital storehouse.

Today the "society where none intrudes" is being penetrated by submarines equipped with nuclear reactors and rockets, by oceanographers with silken dip nets, by oil-drill islands built to hurricane specifications, and by scuba divers clad in pastel neopreme suits. "A complete three-dimensional realm for the military, commercial, scientific and recreational operations of man," exults Seabrook Hull, a new-style ocean admirer, in his book *The Bountiful Sea.* A "sea of profit" gloats a Wall Street broker. Even the Boy Scouts offer a new merit badge for oceanography.

The technological penetration of the ocean is daring, inspiring, and, quite possibly, potentially disastrous. If the ocean is to be a jumbo resource, its exploitation must be carefully husbanded. The ocean can no longer take care of itself. It requires as much respect for its weakness as its strength. The concept of an all-powerful ocean is today obsolete.

The challenge of conserving as well as exploiting the ocean weighs heavily on the United States. This country began as a maritime nation, something that seems inconceivable after a visit to the inevitable slum of any city—its waterfront. It will probably survive or end as one. Because of its technology, international politics, and geography, the United States is wedded to its marine destiny. Its eastern coast fronts on the Atlantic Ocean. Its southern coast sits atop the Gulf of Mexico and the Caribbean Sea. Its western coast confronts the North Pacific Ocean, the Bering and Chukchi seas, and the Arctic Ocean. Its fiftieth state lies in the Central Pacific, the territory of Guam and the UN trusteeship of Micronesia in the Western Pacific. The United States is part of a continent. It is also a big island surrounded by two oceans and a host of seas and gulfs; and in the middle of this big island lie the Great Lakes, a vast system of waterways, which helps to nourish the oceans through the mouth of the St. Lawrence River. Yet we jeopardize this fantastic marine patrimony if we can spud submarine oil wells but cannot conserve sea forests.

The challenge of the ocean is international as well as national in scope. As marine technology generates more activities and ambitions, nations must learn how to preserve marine resources as well as their respective tempers. Nutrition experts promote the ocean as a food locker for future survival, but the high seas fishery competition seems little related to effective conservation or food distribution. The ocean promises to be the ultimate challenge to nations to coexist on a watery planet whirling through space. An indication of the ultimate seriousness of this challenge is that three estranged world powers, the United States, Mainland China, and Russia, now share a common border—the Pacific Ocean—perhaps the planet's richest resource.

A rather ominous question emerges. Byron claimed that "Man marks the earth with ruin." Many of our hills, valleys, and rivers—even the air we breathe—today testify grotesquely to the accuracy of his pessimism. Are we perhaps fated to mark the ocean with ruin, to plunder, pollute, and contend until we have a ghost ocean bereft of all but the voice of its waves?

To avoid such a fate will require comprehensive planning and policy making. Yet before rational planning can take place we must understand the ocean, its tolerances and stresses as well as its wealth. It would be comforting to find that man, spurred on by his intense and probing curiosity, was already busily divining and heeding these tolerances. Yet time and time again sanitary outfall engineers, fishermen, dredge operators, marine miners, oceanographers, and breakwater designers who think they understand the ocean must stand back and wonder, "How did that happen?"

2.

The Tainted Sea

THE sea is not always blue. Sometimes it is stained with a dull red that shrimp fishermen compare with tobacco juice and tourists with tomato soup. In the evening a much more dazzling color may emerge. A wave that feels the bottom, crests, and topples will release a phosphorescent surf of pale green or red hue. This glowing, advancing surf can be stunning, like lambent lightning across the sky or a rainbow on the horizon. Once, while viewing this radiance from a Malibu beach, I happened to glance back over my shoulder and noticed that my footprints also glowed for an instant in the wet sand.

To the residents of the Florida Gulf Coast a dull red sea is far more than just a curiosity, for it signifies the advent of a distressing chain of events commonly referred to as the "red tide." Amazed fishermen watch schools of mullet suddenly splashing about in a frenzy. Some leap out of the water, as if trying to escape their very home. This frantic activity gradually subsides, as fish after fish begins to float belly up. Soon a windrow of dead fish winds through the reddish sea. The entire school has perished.

9

Like a massive janitor's broom, the tides and the winds sweep fish windrow after fish windrow onto the glistening white Gulf beaches. Municipal bulldozers and roadscrapers hastily push the stinking, sun-basted windrows into lime-filled pits. An odorless and colorless gas, swirling above this makeshift burial ground, causes beach visitors and vendors to tear, gasp, gag, and even vomit. Motel operators and hotel managers are besieged by guests suddenly turned hostile. The beauty of the night-tide surf hardly serves to compensate for the other properties of the red tide.

Although of little solace to a motel operator counting canceled vacation reservations, the phenomenon of discolored water—the scientifically accepted phrase for red tide—appears throughout the world. It occurs in a variety of shades and has been doing so for some time. The *Iliad* spoke of the Mediterranean's changing color, and the seventh chapter of Exodus observed the same chameleon quality on the lower Nile:

> And all of the waters that were in the river were turned to blood and the fish that was in the river died; and the river stank, and the Egyptians could not drink of the water of the river.

What this did to the Nile tourist trade is not mentioned.

The sea can and does turn white off Ceylon, yellow off Brazil, green off Spain, black off western Africa, and dull red off California. Puget Sound, in the state of Washington, and Delaware and Narragansett bays on the eastern seaboard are also afflicted by "bloody waters." The sea turns red off Peru, but Peruvians call the lethal tide *el pintor*, in honor of the sulfurous fumes of accompanying decay that blacken ship's brass.

Although discolored water is worldwide, its impact on sea life varies enormously. In some areas it remains unaffected, and sea breezes stir as fresh as ever. In others discolored water mocks the ocean's beauty and fertility and indulges in an orgy of destruction. "The sea just gives up and dies," observed one perplexed oceanographer. That this is the occasional lot of Florida Gulf

Coast waters is of great concern to state officials. In the pecking order of state problems one official has ranked the red tide as "second only to the weather." Such lofty concern has fostered a major attempt to eradicate the ocean's most incongruous phenomenon.

The Florida Gulf Coast has always considered itself blessed by its proximity to the Gulf of Mexico. "There seems to be no end to the oysters, the fish, the sea birds, the shells, the turtles along these waters," exulted Sidney Lanier, commissioned a century ago by the Atlantic Seaboard Railroad to write about the Florida Gulf Coast. Lanier was even more impressed by the coastline itself, grooved with spacious bays, rimmed by endless white beaches, and shadowed by leafy palms and sprawling mangrove trees. "This suave region," declared the poet-promoter, "is a sort of Arabian nights, vaguely diffused and beaten out into a long, glittering, sleepy expanse and the waters presently cease to be waters and seem only great level enchantments-that-shine."

Cities devoted to cultivating such assets have long since sprung up: St. Petersburg, Pensacola, Tampa, Sarasota. Fishing fleets take mullet, red snapper, menhaden, and shrimp. Descendants of Greek divers venture out in boats called *Venus, Apollo,* and *Bozzaris* to dive to the rich sponge beds off Tarpon Springs. New York bankers and retired Chicago shopkeepers risk blisters and coronaries to pole marlin, sailfish, and the "silver king" of leaping sportfish, the tarpon. No coastline in the United States is favored with such a variety of marine species—more than three hundred of them.

Already a prominent fish hole and retirement haven (shuffleboard clubs in St. Petersburg boast memberships of three thousand plus), the Florida Gulf Coast now seeks to market its marine surroundings as a setting for industries that shape advanced technology. Toledo, Grand Rapids, Chicago, and St. Paul may have plenty of coal, iron, and synthetic rubber, but the Gulf Coast possesses the resource of the future—a marketable environment that can snare choosy scientists and engineers.

There is nothing like a sunny beach and blue waves to spruce up a recruitment brochure.

The ominous red blemish on these southern waters first appeared in 1946. Up until that time the Florida Gulf Coast had considered itself relatively immune to red tides, the last one having appeared in 1932, the one before that in 1916. But in November the water began turning red, and the severity of the ensuing red tide shattered any complacency. Dead fish accumulated on the Fort Meyers shoreline at the rate of a hundred pounds per linear foot. A windrow ten yards wide stretched for some five miles on one beach. Road scrapers worked furiously to avert a public health menace. On serene Captiva Island one homeowner had to bury sixty thousand fish before regaining the use of his sandy front yard. Amid the piles of mullet and snapper lay the bloated forms of once-magnificent tarpon and frisky porpoises. Only true crabs and sponges managed to escape the vast marine purge. Biologist Gordon Gunter's conservative estimate was fifty million dead fish.

The red tide outbreak was not only severe but of long duration, lingering on until August of 1947, a period of ten months. The outbreak quickly assumed an exasperating economic form. Sport-boat skippers would take out a dwindling number of clients to catch snapper or tarpon. Whenever their boats passed through a reddish patch, the live bait in the stern tanks would suddenly splash spasmodically and then perish en masse. The water pump designed to keep the tank water fresh had cycled in a dose of the deadly red water. Skippers were forced to tell their clients that they could no longer offer them the means to catch whatever fish had managed to evade the red tide. Commercial fishing as well as sport fishing was sharply curtailed.

On shore the stinking beaches and choking air took their own toll. Demand for tourist accommodations in St. Petersburg almost stopped in one six-week period. Hotel and motel managers in Fort Meyers reported a half-million-dollar loss in canceled reservations. Real estate prices in Sarasota plummeted. The fact that bathers could swim in the red waters and that vacationing fishermen could eat fish caught in them was of little consolation. If the stinking windrows and the invisible gas did not discourage Gulf visitors, the thick slimy nature of the discolored water usually did. "When taken up in the hand," noted Robert Ingle of the Florida State Board of Conservation, "the water runs from the fingers in strings like thin syrup." For travel agents the region was becoming a place to send expendable clients. The Florida Gulf Coast's prize asset, its waters, was contriving to place the region under economic quarantine.

Distress over the red tide was intensified by the fact that no one could fathom its cause. Rumor soon had it that the red tide was a Russian form of chemical warfare. This set others to speculating that the U.S. Navy had made a miscalculation during similar experiments. Almost routinely, atomic fallout was added to the rumor mill. A charge that particularly appealed to consumers was that fishermen were dumping their catches to keep prices high. But the rumor with the most staying power maintained that dumped nerve gas was the cause. The genesis of this theory lay in the fact that the Army had dumped quantities of nerve gas into the Gulf.

Added to the clamor of rumors were demands that the State Division of Salt Water Fisheries and the U.S. Fish and Wildlife Service poison, spray, disinfect or otherwise treat the red tide. Initially, these agencies were ill-equipped to cope with it. Although the United States began as a maritime nation, its interests—scientific as well as economic—have gravitated to land resources. Consequently the Department of Agriculture can sponsor broad scientific investigations, but the U.S. Fish and Wildlife Service and its state counterparts have too often been restricted to stocking fresh-water lakes with trout. This may have placated sport-fishing clubs, but it has hardly fostered a useful appreciation or understanding of the ocean.

Marine biologists from state and federal agencies were soon able to absolve Russia and the United States Navy. ("The Red Tide has nothing to do with Communism," observed *Science Newsletter* drily.) They were also able to squelch the nerve-gas rumor. The Army had indeed dumped nerve gas into the Gulf, but some three hundred miles away, off Mobile, and well after the initial red-tide outbreak.

A university biologist even succeeded in identifying the principal agent of death. Dr. C. C. Davis found one marine organism teeming in the red waters. Gymnodinium breve (nicknamed "Jim Brevis") measures one thousandth of an inch in width. This organism was tinting the Gulf red and killing fish by the millions.

G. breve belongs to the dinoflagellates (whirling organisms with whiplike appendages), an uncommonly talented class of plankton. Like plants, dinoflagellates use sunlight to transform sea nutrients into energy (photosynthesis). A red eyespot guides them to their proper light levels. Like animals, dinoflagellates are mobile, driven by currents, winds and their slim whiplike appendages. Under a microscope they are as exquisite as tiny jewel boxes. These unique organisms, half-animal, half-plant, drift cloudlike inside the sea, fine as fog, providing good grazing for fish and baleen whales.

These clouds can, however, burst into frantic fertility. *G. breve* will suddenly jump from one thousand to the quart to an incredible sixty million. A "bloom" becomes so dense that the eyespots of its members color the sea.

Some blooms, particularly those off California, emit a green or red phosphorescence. Sailors once regarded this nighttime radiance as the reflected flames of hell. One can even read a newspaper in the brilliance of a bloom in a Puerto Rican bay. The reason for such brilliance is not well understood; with their high phosphorous content, dinoflagellates may be literally striking themselves like matches. *G. breve* is not considered luminous; this quality in a Florida red tide comes from another dinoflagellate.

Most blooms provide a magnificent banquet for fish and whales. Others breed death, and the blooms of *G. breve* fall into this death-dealing category. *G. breve* blooms excrete a waste that immobolizes the nervous systems of fish, including their gills. This nerve toxin accounts for the spasmodic dance of the mullet just before death. The massive decomposition that results from the fish pogroms has another lethal aspect. At the same time that the products of decomposition provide more fuel for the blooms, the process of decomposition itself exhausts the oxygen content of the water and serves to suffocate the fish that have not yet breathed the toxin.

After the ominous rumors of atomic fallout and dumped nerve gas the residents of the Florida Gulf Coast had difficulty in believing that an invisible organism could be fostering the red tide and jeopardizing their sunshine and retirement economy. For the scientists the identification of the cause of the red tide led only to a more difficult question: what caused the G. breve to bloom? Blooms of dinoflagellates are as natural as the budding of flowers or the occurrence of earthquakes. The combinations of causative possibilities were almost infinite: winds, weather, supply of nutrients, light conditions, salinity, and so on. A precise knowledge of sea processes was a prerequisite to deciphering the G. breve blooms, and knowledge gained from trout-propagation programs and oyster-bed cultivation was hardly equal to this task. Obviously a major research program was in order. Scientists, unfortunately, were unable to cultivate G. breve in the laboratory, a situation that effectively cramped research once a red tide—with its abundant supply of G. breve specimens—had ebbed.

The residents of the Florida Gulf Coast thought there was a better way of dealing with this phenomenon—writing it off as a freakish occurrence. After all, only three had occurred in an equal number of decades. Four years then passed without another outbreak. A government laboratory studying G. breve blooms was closed for purposes of economy. Shortly afterward, the sea off Fort Meyers again turned red. Only a seaward wind prevented fish corpses from inundating the beaches. A year later, another red tide bloomed. This time the winds were blowing the other way. The roadscrapers were back in business on the beaches. The following year, 1954, a new red tide ranged from Sarasota to Fort Meyers—a span of fifty miles—and extended as far as fifteen miles out to sea. An extensive fish kill and clean-up ensued.

In the manner of a chamber of commerce dealing with a local hurricane, the tendency was to play down the reappearance of the red tide in order to stave off national publicity. But soon a group of Florida organizations petitioned President Eisenhower for federal money to control the latest bloom, which threatened "to make three hundred miles of highly developed Florida coastline uninhabitable." "Panic in Paradise" was the way one journalist sized up the local reaction.

Eight years after the 1946 outbreak the Fish and Wildlife Service was finally able to mount a modest research program. Cultures of *G. breve* were cultivated in laboratories as carefully as "orchids in a hothouse" to permit year-round study. All the moods of the sea—temperature, salinity, winds, and currents—were systematically observed and recorded in an attempt to isolate circumstances associated with *G. breve* blooms. A daily sea was virtually recreated on graph paper.

Gradually, a pattern began to emerge. Two of the severest red-tide outbreaks occurred in 1947 and 1953, years in which Florida's annual rainfall topped sixty inches, well above normal. Under the impact of the rain clouds the Peace River discharged into the Gulf at the rate of two thousand cubic feet per second, twice its rate during dry years. The correspondence between red-tide outbreaks and high rainfall led to an interesting speculation. Was the resulting high runoff from lands and rivers injecting massive doses of nutrients into the sea and "fertilizing" *G. breve* blooms? Suspicion began centering on phosphate, one particular nutrient in river discharges supplied copiously by inland phosphate mines. Such suspicion was allayed, however, by two subsequent disclosures. Red tides bloomed in waters low in phosphate content, and researchers discovered that seafloor deposits already supplied ample amounts of phosphate.

On the other hand, trace elements of iron, another

ingredient of river discharges, was in much less generous sea supply. Researchers in the laboratory noted that iron stimulated the growth of *G. breve*. Another ingredient of high runoff, tannic acid, tended to make trace iron more soluble in seawater and thus more available to *G. breve*.

Researchers found that a prominent by-product of bacterial action in bays and harbors—vitamin B_{12}—also contributed to the growth of *G. breve*. The quiet, settling waters of bays and harbors could foster *G. breve* concentrations and thus make the B_{12} available for bloom enrichment.

While potential causes began to proliferate like *G. breve* blooms public pressure to control these deadly blossoms increased. The Fish and Wildlife Service and the State Board of Conservation found themselves trying to stamp out a scourge they were unable to explain. Setting natural predators on pests is one patented method of control. Unfortunately, the chief predator on the microscopic *G. breve* is another microscopic dinoflagellate, the luminous *Noctiluca*, which cannot be cultivated in predatory quantities. Chemical control agents can counteract known toxins, but even the Army's chemical warfare branch has failed to isolate and chemically identify *G. breve* toxin.

Prospective control measures then escalated to the extermination of the *G. breve* blooms themselves. Copper sulfate crystals can control algal blooms in lakes, observed researchers; why not *G. breve* blooms? Ernest Mitts of the Florida State Board of Conservation eagerly explained a heartening experiment to reporters. Within seconds after a copper penny was dropped into a quart of sea water containing sixty million *G. breve* all the *G. breve* perished. In 1957 a red tide obligingly appeared for field tests. Some fifty thousand dollars was released from a state red-tide emergency fund to underwrite an airborne assault by the Fish and Wildlife Service. Airplanes carrying tons of copper sulfate flew out over the ocean. Crop-dusting pilots, accustomed to guiding on orange-tree groves, were led to random red sea patches by smoke bombs dropped by spotter planes. A brilliant blue cloud of copper sulfate crystals descended on the patches. The control program, billed as the largest in marine history, at first fulfilled official hopes. The reddish patches vanished. "I think we have seen, in the last week and a half, the beginning of the end of the red tide as a menace to Florida," John Evans of the Fish and Wildlife Service told a reporter for *The Fisherman*. Unfortunately, within a week, the reddish patches reappeared. The copper sulfate had precipitated to the sea floor, a region shunned by *G. breve*. Spraying costs spiraled to one thousand and fifty dollars per square mile, a rather expensive proposition in dealing with a phenomenon of one hundred-square-mile dimensions. "In conclusion, we cannot recommend the dusting of copper sulfate as a control for a red tide outbreak of serious proportions," stated a Fish and Wildlife report coauthored by Mr. Evans.

The Fish and Wildlife Service then began a study of other measures of control. At last count the compounds tested numbered nearly five thousand. It seems that a certain compound in the Gulf waters inhibits toxic ambitions, but it has yet to be identified. Carbonic acid, the one control candidate that fulfills toxic requirements of one hundred per cent lethality in twenty-four hours, also happens to be toxic to agency budgets and to shrimp, the Gulf's most valuable marine crop.

A new approach in control programs has emerged from the association of red-tide outbreaks with high river discharges. Florida officials now feel that by a system of river dams high flow periods could be discharged over a number of months. Such river regulation would reduce the flow of *G. breve* nutrients such as tannic acid and B_{12}. *G. breve* would thus be placed on a diet—a diet enforced by dams. (A corollary project may involve the placement of giant air-bubbling hoses in the bays to induce motion and reduce *G. breve* and B_{12} concentrations.)

Besides requiring a major state expenditure, a dietary

dam system would entail certain risks. The dams would
have to be carefully located and regulated not to flood
out or dry up the estuaries, the nurseries of the sea. (As
Chapter 3 will reveal, however, dams do not combine
well with beaches either. Indeed, the Gulf beaches, as
well as *G. breve*, might wind up on a starvation diet.)
Perhaps most ominously, the dams may turn into a case
of putting out the fire by burning the building down.
Dr. George Rounsefell of the University of Alabama, a
veteran of red-tide investigations, notes that it can be
quite difficult "to distinguish the poison ivy from the
alfalfa." The importance of *G. breve*, trace iron, tannic
acid, and B_{12} in the marine food chain is not precisely
understood. Severe restrictions on their abundance
might restrict the general fertility of the Gulf waters.

The acceptance of such large costs and risks becomes
questionable in light of the actual damage caused by red
tides. The large-scale fish kills have not resulted in any
long-term reduction on commercial fish catches. Far from
being rendered uninhabitable, the Florida Gulf Coast
continues to grow bullishly. National articles with titles
like "Blood in the Gulf" have failed to discourage mi-
grants.

Why, if the red tide appears as nothing more than a
mystifying nuisance, is Florida preparing to escalate
from municipal roadscrapers to public dams? The answer lies partly in the aftermath of an oyster-gathering
party on a bar in Little Sarasota Bay in December 1962.
After collecting about one and one half bushels of oysters, a family of three began consuming the harvest—
both raw and roasted—at the rate of ten to fifteen per
meal. Soon they experienced a tingling sensation in the
face that spread to the fingers and toes. Hot coffee tasted
cold, and a cold drink of water seemed to "burn" the
throat. Diarrhea set in. The father had difficulty keeping
his car on the right side of the road, and his nineteen-
year-old son complained of feeling drunk.

These symptoms all subsided within a day or so, but
the Charlotte County Health Department was disturbed

enough to send refrigerated oyster samples to the Public Health Service's research branch in Cincinnati. The Taft Sanitary Engineering Center injected extracts from the oysters into mice. The mice died, but not instantly as they would have of paralytic shellfish poison. Death was preceded by four hours of labored breathing, a symptom that suggested a poison called ciguatera. Ciguatera's unpredictable occurrence in barracuda, snapper, and reef fishes in tropical areas has already produced elaborate taboos that frustrate attempts to expand South Sea fisheries.

Researchers were unable to determine where the oysters picked up such toxicity. When it was noted, however, that its emergence coincided with a red-tide outbreak, G. breve extracts were injected into mice. The same deadly symptoms recurred. The oysters of Little Sarasota Bay were apparently not only picking up G. breve toxin but were concentrating it into levels harmful to man.

As a result of this perilous magnification, the harvesting of mussels, clams, and other shellfish is prohibited between the months of May and September on the California coast. These shellfish too effectively concentrate toxins secreted by dinoflagellates peculiar to the Pacific Coast. Before the prohibition some three hundred forty-six cases of shellfish poisoning were reported, twenty-four ending in death. "The afflicted person acts as though he were drunk," says zoologist Eugene Bouvee of the University of California at Los Angeles. "No antidote for this poisoning is known." The occurrence of ciguateralike poison in shellfish exposed to G. breve has shaken the original assumption that their blooms could not be toxic to man. Man can apparently swim safely in waters tainted by the bloom, yet become sick after eating a juicy clam plucked from identical waters.

The periodic closure of shellfish harvesting areas has become a new and unfortunate feature of red-tide outbreaks in Florida. Concern over these outbreaks is further heightened by an ominous recitation. Red-tide outbreaks of varying severity have occurred in 1952, 1953,

1954, 1957, 1958, 1959, 1960, 1961, 1962, 1963, and 1964. What was once only rarely seen has now become a feature of the Florida Gulf Coast as common as mangrove trees and tarpon. This situation inspires haunting speculation. Will the cycle of red tides recede to pre-1946 levels or will it intensify—intensify in severity and duration as well as in frequency—and thus imperil the Gulf Coast's "great level enchantments-that-shine"? Do man's increasing waste discharges into ocean-bound rivers account for such an upward cycle or is it propelled by forces that heed only the impersonal laws of nature? Unable to answer these questions, Florida finds itself seriously considering such expensive and risky projects as regulating the diet of a microscopic creature by means of dams. The Gulf of Mexico may be able to take red tides in stride, but Florida feels it cannot afford such nonchalance.

Meanwhile, red tides in southern California are on the increase. The offending dinoflagellate in this area is *Gonyaulax polyhedra*. Perplexed investigators with the California State Fish and Game Department cannot very well implicate river discharges in *G. polyhedra* blooms. As the California beaches demonstrate so well, river runoff has been virtually dammed up. The quiet settling waters of harbors and proliferating marinas are suspects; under consideration is the use of bubbling air hoses to agitate the calm waters. Recent red-tide outbreaks have left ten million fish floating belly up in harbor waters. The Sea World Oceanarium in San Diego was forced on one occasion to cancel half its shows. The star performer, a female pilot whale housed in an ocean-connected lagoon, died in the wake of a red-tide outbreak. Oceanarium officials blamed the death on *G. polyhedra*. As in Florida, such monumental kills generate public pressure on conservation officials. "But stopping a red tide," says John Carlisle of the Fish and Game Department, "is like trying to stop an earthquake."

Red-tide outbreaks off Peru pose a grave problem. Over the last decade Peru has surpassed the United States, Russia, Communist China, and Japan in annual fish landings, with 9.1 metric tons. That Peru paces world fishing activity is all the more remarkable, for a single fish, the small anchoveta, ground to fishmeal, is responsible. The susceptibility of anchoveta to periodic red-tide (*el-pintor*) outbreaks jeopardizes the stability of the world's leading fishmeal industry. Another major industry is similarly affected. Cormorants feed on the anchoveta and then deposit their excrement on "guano island." These prodigious droppings support a flourishing fertilizer industry. When the sea turns red, Peruvians worry, not about show whales and the tourist trade, but about their country's entire economy. At the same time the world fishmeal and fertilizer markets go into a price tizzy.

Such encounters with the phenomenon of discolored water are instructive to a world with pretensions of conquering the ocean. Twenty-two years after the alarming Florida red tide of 1946–1947 the understanding, prediction, and control of *G. breve* blooms still lie in the future. More appropriate allocation of funds is finally modifying this lingering ignorance. (Although the Fish and Wildlife Service began devoting more substantial resources to investigations by 1954, the Florida State Legislature dallied until 1963 before supporting a large-scale state research project.) The resulting imbalance between public interest in the ocean and public funding of ocean research fosters a disconcerting situation. Although we seem to know a good deal about the ocean as a resource, we know little about the ocean as an environment. As long as this imbalance persists, phenomena like discolored water will rebuke our claims to ocean conquest.

As this imbalance is righted in the Florida red-tide situation, a most ironic situation begins to emerge. Scientists are fascinated by the way in which a marine organism such as *G. breve* can immobilize creatures ten times its size by excreting a toxin. A study of this constant chemical warfare promises to produce a rich source of pharmaceuticals. Dr. Ross Nigrelli of the New York

Aquarium injected poison from a sea cucumber into cancers induced in mice. The cancer tumor stopped growing. Dr. Nigrelli told a *New Yorker* reporter that he has also been able to isolate chemicals in marine organisms "that have antiviral, antimicrobial, tumor-inhibiting, nerve-blocking, and heart-stimulating properties." In another area of investigation Dr. S. H. Hunter of Haskins Laboratory, New York, has been intrigued by marine blooms ever since as a boy he watched purple and green algal blooms in city drainage ditches. Although New York drainage ditches and the Gulf of Mexico suffer from blooms of over-fertility, Dr. Hunter points out that substantial parts of the ocean appear to suffer from under-fertility. If prediction and even control of the red tide materializes, Dr. Hunter wonders if man may not then be able to "set off nutritious tides, cultivating the sea as we do the land." In the marine realm opportunity and calamity are not far separated.

3.

In Pursuit of Beaches

A BEACH is the ocean's spacious welcome mat. Without beaches, our way to the sea would be impeded by bluffs, jutting rocks, and smashing surf. With beaches, a child can walk to the sea's edge and play tag with summer wavelets.

On these soft-sloping sand carpets barefoot beach browsers seek all the delights of the seashore: suntans, wading, surfboarding, shell collecting, tidepool exploring, volleyball, surf fishing, bikini watching, sea gazing, lobster parties, and ocean sunsets. On any Sunday a public beach—from Jones to the French Riviera—will easily outdraw city parks, national forests, and baseball doubleheaders. Beaches have become the downtowns of leisure.

Beaches survive cresting combers and countless storm tides; summer pleasure jams prove no more difficult. A million walking, strolling, and running footprints can be etched into a beach in a single day. If the tide runs high during the evening, the rumpled beach will be smoothed out like a freshly pressed tablecloth, waiting patiently for the crease of another million footprints.

Beaches require neither forest rangers nor No Smoking signs—just lifeguards.

Such resiliency is really not so surprising. Besides serving as a clamorous clearing house for marine recreation, a beach can protect a coastal community from angry seas as effectively as rock cliffs or million-dollar seawalls. Here hurricane waves dissolve into swirling backwash, exhausted by the buffer of its soft slope.

Yet in the United States in the last twenty years more than two hundred million dollars has been expended in the unlikely name of beach erosion control. Although beaches can endure hurricanes and summer crowds, they cannot withstand tampering with the natural forces that sustain them.

These sustaining forces, unlike the storm forces that wear the shoreline down, are largely invisible to the eye. In fact, beaches possess an elusive, if not illusionary, character. "Beaches," notes oceanographer Willard Bascom, "are ever-changing, restless armies of sand particles always on the move."

Keeping beaches restless is the turbulence of the surf, which follows a pattern in the form of a current running roughly parallel to the shore. This littoral current rolls as powerfully as any major river. The undertows and rip currents that cause lifeguards to clear the waters manifest its power. It is the littoral current that carries away countless millions of sand grains while at the same time depositing sand grains from beaches "upstream." This "conveyor belt of sand," as Bascom describes it, keeps beach sand in motion but beaches intact. The amount of sand carried by the littoral current—referred to as the littoral drift—reaches a million tons of sand annually on some coastlines.

Sand itself is nothing more than mountain boulders ground exceedingly fine by eons of glaciers, blizzards, and frost. Mountain streams and rivers carry away boulder remains. At a river mouth the littoral current sifts through the residue and siltlike particles are allowed to settle out to form deltas. Heavier particles of quartz are carried away. These particles, as tiny as one eighteenth of a millimeter, are the basis of beaches ten miles long and dunes three stories high.

Energized by the turbulence of the surf, fueled by the runoff of rivers, the littoral current can nourish beaches through winter storms and hurricanes. If this current is obstructed, however, two things can happen. A beach may balloon out like an overfed adult or starve away to nothing. For the last twenty years the latter phenomenon has haunted the residents of two modest communities in Southern California.

Surfside and Sunset Beach occupy a narrow stretch of nondescript land which happens to border a beach some two miles long. This beach is spacious—sometimes as wide as a football field. The summer sun is warm, the Pacific surf, exhilarating, and the ocean sunsets, resplendent. All this marine enchantment lies only an hour's drive south from the sprawling ranchhouse tracts of Los Angeles and Long Beach, out of which come families eager for a weekend foothold on the fabled California shoreline but unable to afford Malibu or Newport Beach. They have colonized Surfside and Sunset Beach with modest beach cottages in bright colors—blue, pink, and white. Many sport names—Cruise of the Snark or Sea Bells—and many are decorated inside with clam shells, ceramic fish, and stiff starfish.

The cottages cluster tightly along a narrow road which parallels the beach. Those on the beachside are in Row A. Across the way stands Row B. The paved surface between is interspersed with deliberate bumps to encourage a vehicular snail's pace. The pedestrian in a bathing suit is king here.

During 1944 and 1945 alarmed cottage residents watched their sandy front yard gradually recede. Soon they found themselves directly confronted by the Pacific Ocean. Approximately two hundred thousand cubic yards of sand was hauled in to remedy this exposure. Within two years another load was required in the amount of a million cubic yards.

Beach umbrellas could once more be unfurled, and children returned to erecting sand castles, but the artificial beach proved no more permanent than its natural predecessor. Within five years another artificial beach had to be emplaced.

One early morning in 1961 Clifford Bell felt himself being nudged from sleep. His son was hovering over him, gesturing toward the first floor of their Row B cottage. Bell hastily installed his hearing aid. "My son was saying that the water faucets must be leaking. The downstairs was becoming covered with water." When Bell opened the door of the cottage to check the outside water pipes, he realized—abruptly and with alarm—that the water system was not to blame. "I found myself stepping out into the Pacific surf in my pajamas."

The beach had disappeared for a second time. The urban dwellers in search of fun-in-the-sun found themselves impressed into a relentless siege. "For the next two months I slept with my shovel at my side," recalled Bell. In the respite between high tides Bell and his neighbors—some in troutstream waders—busily filled sandbags and erected a six-foot high seawall with the aid of forklifts. But a train of waves ten feet high and eleven seconds apart repeatedly breached the hastily assembled barrier. Row A then became an impromptu seawall, one that proved sturdier than the sandbags. Pacific combers burst like snowy avalanches on the wooden cottages, churning foundations and beams into flotsam. This flotsam drifted away on the tides to re-emerge as litter and potential firewood on public beaches farther south.

For residents in Row B life along the breaker zone was a mite less destructive. "The storm tides kept flooding the first floor of our cottage and killed off the plants in my back garden," said Bell. "Sometimes the surf would spray up over the sandbag mounds and rain on the roof. I got knocked down a couple of times by this spray and once lost my hearing aid. I even found myself dodging big rocks tossed about by the surf." The storm tides left a curious legacy. "Fish would be all over the road, along with pismo clams some five inches in size." The road, in the words of one journalist, had become a salt-water canal.

As winter storm tides passed and an emergency sand fill restored the beach buffer, the siege at Surfside-Sunset lifted. Bell returned to work after two straight months of filling sandbags.

Beach erosion engineers with the state and the Army Corps of Engineers realized something was dreadfully amiss with the littoral current off southern California. The weather, or lack of it, emerged as one prime cause of trouble. "During the last twenty years, much of southern California has suffered a prolonged drought which has greatly reduced the runoff reaching the ocean," observed Alfred Golze, chief engineer of California's Department of Water Resources.

The two major factors turned out to be man-made rather than natural. Dams set up to impound river water also impound ocean-borne sand sediment. Gone are the days when the Los Angeles River deposited six million cubic yards of sand in the Los Angeles harbor in the wake of heavy rains. "Where are some of our beaches?" asked California Park Director Charles DeTurk, who pays as much as one hundred twenty dollars an inch to acquire precious new public beach frontage. "They lie at the foot of our dams." The Committee on Oceanography–National Academy of Sciences noted, "Runoff control in southern California has cut the supply of sand to nearly zero and, without some intervention, the beaches may seriously deteriorate within the next two decades." Meanwhile the sand that manages to reach the littoral current is impounded by a different sort of dam. As the current courses past a breakwater, Bascom points out, "the wave-created turbulence that holds the sand in suspension ceases, and the particles are deposited just inside the end of the breakwater." A proliferation of inland dams, harbor breakwaters, and other exercises in shore improvement is destroying the shoreline by damming up the littoral drift.

In the light of drought, dams, and breakwaters, the regular disappearance of Surfside-Sunset beach is easily explained. Just north of the beach lies the mouth of a river that today drains into dams many miles distant. Next door to the dusty river bed lies the Anaheim Bay harbor. Surfside-Sunset residents now recognize that the harbor jetty which serves as such a fine fishing platform also intercepts their beach. It also amplifies wave action and, in turn, beach erosion. Paradoxically, the Corps of Engineers, the same agency now trying to stem this erosion, approved the jetty design.

Powerless to nourish the beach, the littoral current can still carry away beach frontage at the rate of fifty feet a year. This erosive power now extends twelve miles downcoast and jeopardizes a four-lane coastal highway, one hundred million dollars in property development, and four public beaches, including the state's most popular. In the next hundred years thirty million cubic yards of sand would be required to avert such a disaster. This sand transfusion would be expensive—seventeen million dollars—and impractical. A desert would have to be excavated.

Where had all the expensively placed Surfside-Sunset sand gone? Fashionable Newport Beach marks the southern boundary of the endangered twelve-mile shoreline. Extending out from the harbor mouth is a huge underwater cleft or "deep," the Newport Submarine Canyon. In underwater dives one can occasionally observe sand avalanching down the canyon walls like a waterfall. The Corps wonders whether Newport Deep is swallowing its preciously placed sand.

Today, a most ambitious beach-erosion control program is underway. Instead of restoring Surfside-Sunset beach with a million cubic yards of sand, the Corps is emplacing four times that amount by pumping out sand stored behind the mischievous harbor jetty. "I don't walk to the surfline anymore," a bemused Bell said of his new four-hundred-foot beach front. "I hike to it." To prevent the new beach from spilling into the Newport Deep, the Corps considered the use of what has been the littoral drift's nemesis. A breakwater would rise upcoast of the gluttonous deep. The sand settling out in the still of the breakwater would be returned—by barge or by pump—

to its original point of departure. The survival of Surfside-Sunset beach, as well as its downcoast, would be ensured by a littoral drift made to run in a circle.

Newport Beach residents originally protested the creation of a "rock curtain" off their scenic shore. However, two severe beach erosion seiges have moderated this concern. Residents now tolerate a series of rocky groins on their fickle shore and are willing to consider a rock curtain when its design and effectiveness can be ascertained.

The Surfside-Sunset project reflects the magnitude of beach-erosion control. It will require some seven million dollars in funds and seven years to complete. Today a dozen similar projects costing more than seventeen million dollars are being implemented to prevent the beaches of California from vanishing in an age of frenetic shore improvement.

Across the continent another state copes with its own distinctive forms of beach improvement. The New Jersey shore consists mainly of a chain of sand islands separated from one another by tidal channels and from the mainland by inlets created by the channels. These sand islands, or "barrier beaches," exist in other eastern and gulf states but not in such numbers. Uninterrupted by rock cliffs, limestone bluffs, and other impediments to shore development, the New Jersey sand islands have been transformed into a hundred-mile long beach resort, featuring such pleasure centers as Atlantic City, Cape May, Ocean City, Asbury Park, Poverty Beach, and Shark River Inlet.

Unfortunately, the barrier beaches, although quite suitable for public bathing, were never really meant to be colonized by hi-rise resorts. In nature's scheme of things these barrier beaches, by absorbing the punishment of twenty-five-foot waves, insulate the mainland from hurricanes and winter storms. Bathers, unlike ten-story hotels, can heed hurricane warnings by leaving.

The real estate suitability of the New Jersey shore is further imperiled by the swift-flowing tidal currents operating in the channels. Incoming channel tides suck the onshore littoral drift into the quiet, settling waters of the channel bays and inlets. Outgoing channel tides carry the drift into the quiet, settling offshore waters. Thus diverted, the New Jersey littoral drift provides the beaches with little more than a starvation diet. As one Corps engineer, C. E. Wicker, observes, "The beaches gain and lose sand whimsically."

The resort promoters of the nineteenth century who transformed New Jersey's sandy islands into the summer salvation of the sweltering East paid little heed to such natural peculiarities. Stout sand dunes that blunted so well the fury of hurricanes were razed in the interests of more beach lots, better ocean views, and easier beach access.

This enterprise resulted in America's discovery of the delights of the seashore in summer. In the North, Long Branch's beach attractions began to outshine those of fabled Saratoga. Long Branch became the site of the summer White House for Presidents Grant, Harrison, Hayes, Garfield, and Wilson. Here Victorian manners collided head-on with beach fashions. A red flag on the beach meant men could swim, a white flag welcomed the ladies. A later and somewhat paradoxical requirement that women could swim only with escorts led to the rise of a controversial profession. It was on the beaches of Long Branch, not in the dance halls of New York, that the gigolo came into prominence in America.

Amid the general rejoicing at the discovery of the seashore an early observation by one of America's first naval heroes went unheeded. Comparing old maps with new ones, Stephan Decatur found that the tip of Cape May had regressed some three miles, sufficient explanation for the disappearance of two lighthouses. This trend did occasionally manage to inspire a benefience in realty developers. After pressing development virtually to the high-tide mark, the developers would deed the remaining narrow shore strip to the local community, which thereupon picked up the supposedly modest maintenance costs.

As a result of such enterprise, New Jersey is blessed with a billion-dollar tourist economy continually threatened with partial or complete extinction. The littoral current constantly chews away at the shoreline, exposing boardwalks time and time again to storm tides. Long Branch's Ocean Avenue has twice been ingested by waves. The borough of South Cape May has fallen into the Atlantic; in nearby Strathmere two Roman Catholic convents, a Coast Guard station, and John Wanamaker's summer cottage face the same fate. What the littoral current has accomplished over the years storms named after lovely ladies can complete in a matter of hours. Governor after governor has been forced to declare the New Jersey shore a disaster area in the wake of a hurricane.

To fly over the New Jersey shore today is to fly over a coastline cluttered with rock groins, steel-sheet pilings, concrete seawalls, rubble revetments, timber bulkheads and other fortifications Winslow Homer had no opportunity to paint. These fortifications, although pictorially impressive, qualify as little more than holding devices. The groins, which extend out from the beach to intercept and hoard the stingy littoral drift for upstream beaches, only compound erosion problems downstream. Downstream beach owners react by erecting their own groins to compete for what little sand is left. As a result, more than three hundred groins in various stages of storm-battered decay protrude from the New Jersey shore.

Like groins, seawalls constitute their own inherent hazards to beach-erosion control. Communities that erect expensive seawalls to protect upland property only jeopardize the natural feature that attracted property development in the first place. The seawalls create a severe surf backwash that accelerates beach erosion. Sand dunes, before being razed, provided identical protection without eroding beaches.

All this brute-force engineering is conducted under the "war" theory of beach-erosion control. Control efforts become "battles," seawalls and groins are "fortifications" or, in England, "sea defence works." The ocean, naturally, becomes the "enemy." Victory is defined as "shore stabilization." Caught up in this martial cant, the Corps of Engineers' Coastal Engineering Research Center (CERC) declares, "Our campaign against the encroachment of the sea must be waged with the same care that we would take against any other enemy threatening our boundaries." Yet under these terms man must qualify as the fifth column, if not the true enemy, for in New Jersey as well as in California he is quite literally battling his own ignorance or disregard of natural beach processes. This ignorance can be contagious. The ephemeral nature of the New Jersey shore spurred summer settlement of the Florida shore and with much the same consequences. At Palm Beach, the elite successor to Cape May and Long Branch, one five-mile stretch of shore features thirty-two shore protection devices.

New Jersey and other eastern states now concentrate more on cooperating with, rather than flaunting, beach processes. Dunes are being protected and restored. Inlets are dredged of sand to create dunes with a base of three hundred feet and a height of eighteen feet along the Long Island shore. Some sixty-eight thousand post-Christmas trees have been placed on the dunes to filter sand out of the sea winds. Although these highly efficient sand catchers were donated by New Yorkers, the Long Island dunes program has still cost millions of dollars in the last ten years.

As in California, massive, and repeated, sand hauls have been required to restore beaches as well as dunes. (Occasionally, like groins, these sand transfusions will boomerang. The Corps of Engineers once dumped six hundred thousand cubic yards of sand a half-mile off the Long Branch shore. Incoming waves were to distribute this sand in a natural pattern along the beach, which loses one hundred fifty-six cubic yards of sand annually. Five years later the corps found their sand pile virtually intact. Waves just could not reach to its thirty-eight-foot depth.) This method of compensating for a scanty littoral drift may well be already obsolete. "Few people realize that sand is a rapidly diminishing natural resource," notes A. C. Rayner in "Land Against the Sea," a CERC publication. "Once carried to our shores in abundant supply by streams, rivers and glaciers, geological processes have progressed to a stage where large areas of our coast receive no supply from this source. All cultural development by man in inland areas tends to further reduce erosion of the upland with resulting reduction in sand supply to the shore."

The search for sand has attained hectic, world-wide proportions. Hawaii's Waikiki Beach must be periodically rebuilt with sand trucked in from dunes fourteen miles away. Island hotel owner Henry Kaiser manufactures his own out of gravel and grit. "In Jamaica," notes William Herron, a Corps engineer active in beach conservation in California, "the authorities just about make you shake out your pants cuffs before you leave the beach." The search for sand has already spawned conflict. To save a San Diego beach shorn of eleven million cubic yards of sand over the last twenty years Corps engineers propose dredging San Diego Bay. The California State Resources Agency, however, opposes this massive project because of the possible destruction of marine life.

Great Britain's eastern shoreline is especially wracked by a skimpy littoral drift and obstinate wave action, courtesy of the North Sea. "The configuration of the coastline of Great Britain is not the same for two consecutive days," notes one scientific observer. The destruction of seven villages along the Holderness Coast, which have fallen into the North Sea, has led to such map notations as "Withernsea—lost by the sea." As in New Jersey, hasty excavation of sand dunes has helped to expedite such abrupt disappearances.

The increasing need for, and expense of, beach conservation raises an issue that the courts have been trying to resolve for some time—who is to foot the bill? Fairness seems to dictate that the owner who erects a shore protection or improvement structure should be liable for any erosive consequences. Yet the courts have felt compelled to take quite the opposite stand.

In the 1820's storm waves stripped away a beach buffer protecting the English community of Pagham. When the sea spilled into coastal lands, a group of property owners persuaded the Pagham Commissioner of Sewers to erect a rock groin. The nature of the groin

immediately asserted itself. While restoring the beach
buffer for upstream owners, it hastened beach erosion
for those downstream. One sand-shorted owner went to
court to seek an order for the destruction of the upsetting
groin. There was little doubt in the court's mind that a
groin, in effect, protected one person's property at the
expense of another's, but abolition of groins would deprive beach owners of a means of self-protection. Concluded Lord Tentreden for the court, "Each landowner
may erect such defenses for the land under their care
as the necessity of the case requires, leaving it to others,
in like manner, to protect themselves against the common
enemy."

This "common-enemy" doctrine legalized shore protection devices and provided historic precedent for the
frantic New Jersey groin race. In essence, anybody who
could not protect his beach property from upstream
owners as well as the sea simply did not belong on the
seashore. The advent of shore improvement structures—
marina breakwaters designed to protect pleasure craft
instead of beaches—presented the courts with a possible
opportunity to soften the somewhat harsh common-
enemy doctrine. In 1929, against the advice of the Corps
of Engineers, Santa Barbara, California, erected a breakwater to shelter small craft and attract tourist income.
The basis of the Corps' concern immediately became
evident. Above the breakwater beach frontage ballooned
out some seven hundred feet. Within the breakwater
sand began shoaling up at the rate of eight hundred cubic
yards a day. Below the breakwater the shore receded as
much as two hundred forty-five feet. Ten miles downstream a row of beach homes slumped into the sea. The
breakwater that cost less than a million dollars to build
caused twice that amount in property damage.

A beach hotel that found itself without a beach decided
to sue the city. But the Miramar lacked the financial
stamina to weather the depression, the breakwater, and
the lengthy litigation. By 1939 the referee in bankruptcy
for the Miramar Company offered to settle the suit for
five hundred dollars. The Santa Barbara city attorney,

perturbed more by a possible adverse decision than by legal costs, counseled acceptance. By the time the apprehensive city council decided to accept the offer, it had been withdrawn. A California State Supreme Court ruling had prompted the referee to reinstitute the seven hundred fifty thousand dollar suit. A number of private beach owners had sued a beach resort for erecting two groins that had "denuded" them of sand. The beach resort claimed they were built in the interest of shore protection and thus came under the common-enemy doctrine, but the plaintiffs pointed out that no beach erosion problem existed. The groins had served to expand resort property about one hundred feet by accreting the sand supply of the plaintiffs. In upholding the suit the court demolished the recourse to the common-enemy doctrine by simply observing, "Tidewaters are not storm waters." This legal distinction between structures built in the interests of shore improvement and those built in the interests of shore protection inspired hope in the referee of the bankruptcy case.

The State Supreme Court, in hearing Miramar Hotel versus Santa Barbara, proceeded to distinguish between private and public shore improvements. Santa Barbara, the court found, is held by law to improve state-owned tidelands under its jurisdiction in the interests of navigation and commerce. The Miramar claim "could not be recognized without creating a servitude in the tidelands inconsistent with the state's title and its rights to erect improvements in the interests of navigation." The court even exempted the public body from the law of eminent domain—just compensation for property taken. This decision seemed too sweeping to one dissenting judge, who observed that a beach owner "certainly has a vested right in past accretion, they having thus become his upland, which may not be taken without the payment of compensation." Predicted the California *Law Review*: "The main opinion in Miramar Hotel versus Santa Barbara, until it is removed by direct repudiation, will be a source of confusion. . . ."

Instead of being repudiated, the opinion has been

expanded. When Santa Monica's harbor breakwater fostered a five-hundred-foot accretion of sand in front of a local beach club, the club claimed the accretion as an extension of its property, but a court said that the claim would deprive the city of land it had created on its own tidelands. Today the club no longer borders on the ocean. To reach the water, a club member must thread his way through one of southern California's most popular public beaches.

In paying such close attention to the public interest in shore improvements, the courts have permitted coastal cities to indulge quite recklessly in shore destruction. Santa Barbara has finally restored the ten miles of beach its breakwater undermined. This restoration, effected by a harbor sand by-passing system through dredging, came a good decade after the two million dollars in damages had occurred and was inspired less by a sense of obligation than by Federal aid and the need to keep the harbor filled with water rather than sand.

The crucial responsibility of beach conservation has too often been allowed to rest on those least equipped to handle it. Seaside communities as well as individuals have gone into debt to offset the impact of massive public exercises in shore improvement. (Some coastal hamlets in England are bonded to their seawalls.)

The governmental body best equipped to deal with the technical, economic, and political challenge of beach erosion has only lately realized that beaches can be as important as harbors. Although Congress authorized the Corps of Engineers to provide technical assistance to communities beset by beach erosion back in 1930, it was not until 1962 that it offered a more substantial form of assistance. In March of that year an Atlantic storm sent twenty-foot waves crashing into the eastern seaboard for a period of two days. On learning that beach conservation projects, starving for funds, could have greatly reduced storm damage, Congress authorized the Federal Government to finance up to seventy per cent of the proposed work. Today this authorization supports more than fifty projects, including one at Surfside-Sunset.

The cost of beach erosion control is still prohibitive for some beach communities. In explaining denial of Federal support for needed million-dollar jetties in the beleaguered Cape May Point area, Frank Sivard of the Corps of Engineers declared, "It comes down to the fact that Atlantic City serves more people than the beaches of Cape May Point would; therefore, it can get more Federal aid. This is one of the facts of life. It is a brutal fact."

The Corps is trying to apply modern technology to beach conservation. To understand shore processes better, the Corps has built a wave tank at the CERC that generates six-foot waves. A shore-process test basin duplicates entire shorelines. The Corps is also expanding the search for sand. More than two hundred geological borings have been taken off New Jersey shore in waters as deep as one hundred feet and as far out as thirty miles. One boring uncovered a potentially important sustainer of the New Jersey shore, a sand shoal containing forty million cubic yards of sand.

Unfortunately, Corps efforts in harbor systems (one hundred eighty million dollars annually) give Corps efforts directed at beach erosion control (four million dollars annually) a Jekyll and Hyde quality—witness the mischievous Anaheim Bay jetty. President Johnson's prestigious advisory Panel on Oceanography reports, "The Panel was distressed to find a high failure rate of construction projects in the surf zone and on beaches. The destruction of beaches by breakwaters designed to extend them, the silting of harbors and marinas as a result of construction designed to provide shelter, and the intensification of wave action by the building of jetties supposed to lessen wave action are but a few examples of the inadequacy of our knowledge and practice in coastal construction." (Enhancing the erosive power of tidal channels by deepening them for marina purposes is another example, prevalent in Florida and New Jersey.) "There is need to enhance research at CERC," continues the Panel. "Its small budget cannot possibly underwrite the research and development required. . . . The Panel believes that standards of coastal engineering can be

raised only by active participation of university groups."
Dr. D. L. Inman of Scripps Institution, who studies
beach problems (including those of the Corps) observes,
"We are in the curious position of developing and improving beach frontage without criteria for predicting
changes in the beach or evaluating the likelihood of the
beach's existence in ten or twenty years."

The Corps' ability to control beach erosion is further
handicapped by its inability to prevent such erosion in
the first place. In the popular cant of beach erosion control, the Corps is inheriting a "frontline" that is being
constantly overextended by resort developers, marina
promoters, and ambitious coastal cities such as Santa
Barbara which fail to heed Corps counsel. Two potential
disrupters of the littoral drift—coastal causeways and
artificial islands for oil wells and power plants—enjoy
increasing civic favor. Outflanked by hurricanes, breakwaters, dams, and artificial islands, the Corps will have
to reinforce an impotent littoral drift with larger and
lengthier sand convoys. In time the Corps may even become the littoral drift.

Many public officials are excited over the perched
beach concept. This concept would create offshore
beaches "perched on" or supported at the seaward end
by a solid submerged dike extending some distance above
the natural floor. The California Division of Highways
wants to build such a beach as a replacement for a
natural beach in the Los Angeles area sought as a freeway right-of-way. However, a principle originator of the
concept, Dr. Inman, warns the concept needs considerable experimentation. The natural sand transport could
be shunted to deep waters. The submerged dike could
also foster destructive instead of constructive wave action.

At the precise moment that their ultimate survival is
in doubt, beaches are in greater demand than ever. Indeed, these downtowns of leisure are deteriorating into
sweaty Sunday ghettos, where barefoot pedestrians wait
in line for parking places, hi-rise rest stations, and waves.
Homer's airy representations of life on the Long Branch

beach have been supplanted by Reginald Marsh's garish, limb-tangled representations of life at Rockaway and Coney Island. Such scenes were not made inevitable by increasing population; our disregard of beach processes contributes greatly to the waiting lines.

A better appreciation of beach processes might have forestalled the bulldozing of the sand dunes, the erection of breakwaters without facilities for sand to bypass them, the overdevelopment of barrier beaches, and the frantic New Jersey groin race. Our desire to exploit the ocean and its resources, however, always races ahead of our full and necessary understanding of its processes.

4.

Of Sea Forests and
Sea Rangers

WHEN I enter a forest on land, I feel like an intruder, as I crunch dead twigs and dry leaves underfoot and send deer and birds into flight. But there is a sense of privilege in descending quietly into a sea forest. If my air tank brushes a frond, it continues to sway, and the forest's inhabitants—from darting perch to rockbound starfish—remain unperturbed. A seal may speed torpedolike toward me, only to arc away in a playful somersault, as if he were bounding off a trampoline. Here I feel tolerated, not resented, free to glide through a wilderness that hides nothing from the visitor.

Although native to coastlines throughout the Southern Hemisphere, these convivial forests of giant kelp fringe only one coastline in the Northern Hemisphere, an exception generally credited to the Ice Age. Kelp abhors tepid water, and the Ice Age is believed to have provided the chill that enabled kelp from the western coast of South America to bound across the equator and colonize the western coast of North America. In southern California, where advanced technology reigns supreme in both recreation and industry, the North American sea forests have been explored, enjoyed, harvested, exploited, and desecrated in a manner that conforms with their remarkable bounty and their convenient offshore location.

That a seaweed can form a forest beneath the ocean may seem improbable to any one whose acquaintance with these plants is limited to the beach. A child may triumphantly lash the sand with a whiplike kelp frond or gleefully pop the odd hollow bulbs that cluster on it, but to most beach visitors a clump of drift kelp, which manages to support a black halo of swarming flies, merits the attention only of beach clean-up crews. Not until the emergence of scuba-diving technology did I discover myself that kelp in its proper environment can be as fascinating as that popular ocean symbol, the coral bed. Because kelp grows in water no deeper than one hundred feet, the sea forests off southern California lie within reach of anyone willing to swim through the breaker zone. Once beyond the thunder of the surf, the swimmer can emplace his face mask and look below. Here, under the sea, the kelp unfurls, rising from a bottom anchorage or "holdfast" to the ocean surface in long leafy vines called fronds which spread over the water like ivy to form a thick brown canopy. Leaves—or blades —three feet long extend like streamers from the frond. One frond can measure more than two hundred feet, and as many as one hundred fronds will rise from just one kelp plant. The curious bulbs I once popped on the seashore serve as floats that buoy up the rangy fronds. These underwater plants grow six feet apart, and a sea forest of kelp plants can cover an area as wide as eight square miles.

The canopy shrouds the sun and the light sieves through in beams and rays. In this shifting light the brown of the kelp seems to alter, wavering between green and blue and copper. Under an intense sun, the kelp glows yellow, and the underwater wanderer finds himself zigzagging through a golden forest set against a marine blue backdrop. This forest is always in motion, yet no leaves rustle or limbs creak. The three-hundred-pound kelp plants oscillate gently, enveloped in the silence so common to the inner ocean.

James Stewart, the diving officer at Scripps Institution of Oceanography, compares passing through a lush kelp forest to "swimming through a bowl of spaghetti." Anyone who underestimates the hazards of this dense foliage does so at considerable risk. I have before me a Los Angeles *Times* newsclip that describes how a thirty-five-year-old man, equipped with only a snorkel (surface) breathing device, became entangled in kelp fronds on a short dive below the surface. He thrashed about desperately to reach a breath of air just ten feet above him. A companion diver, tried frantically to break the grip of the fronds. The clip is headlined "Mesh of Kelp Brings Death to Skin Diver." A second newsclip, dated a month before the first, details how another skin diver became entrapped as irrevocably as an insect in a spider web.

Life in a sea forest rises toward the top in sharp gradations of movement. Brittle stars, purple sea fans, lavender sponges, ostrich-plume hydroids, flowery sea anemones, and lobsterlike crayfish ring the rockbound holdfast. Above this almost immobile layer of life cruise small sand sharks and rays flapping their robelike wings like finny Draculas. Above them schools of shimmering sardines pass like rain showers, and bass, sheepshead, spiny sculpin, and dainty senoritas dart about. On the outskirts of the forest bonita, barracuda, and albacore sprint like animated steel arrows, and above the surface the seabird swirls, occasionally lighting on the brown canopy.

In a sea forest the struggle for survival rushes up and down a sixty-foot column of water like a busy elevator. The seabirds dive-bomb baby bass exposed by an opening in the canopy, and bonita and barracuda pounce on them as they stray out of the sea forest. Inside the forest a bass may saunter by with a perch wriggling between its jaws. The more fortunate perch, meanwhile, fatten up on bottom shrimp and scallops and nibble on kelp blades.

The colors of marine life in a sea forest are muted, as they are in so much of nature. The fish and bottom creatures adopt the shades of the forest: mottled browns, dark yellows, dusky oranges, and rock grays. Occasionally, a garabaldi, an oversized goldfish, will spurt around like a spark in search of a fire, but such ostentation is the exception. The blend of color explains why I prefer kelp forests to the more popular coral beds. Although the coral beds of the tropical seas flaunt a dazzling array of colors, like rainbows shattered into a million broken glints, they appear to be the creation not of nature but of a precocious child or of Walt Disney. The kelp forest unfolds as a natural wilderness, marine-style.

The prize game in this wilderness is the black bass, which can weigh more than four hundred pounds. Its hunter uses a spear gun six feet long which springs a six-inch steel shaft attached to one hundred fifty feet of high-test nylon line. When the bass glides within range (eight yards), the hunter triggers the silent gun, and the shaft leaps the gap. Landing a bull's-eye shot at the backbone behind the gills is only part of the job. To shake loose the steel shaft, the bass will tow the hunter on a frantic underwater ride. If his air supply holds and he can steer the bass into a mesh of kelp, which will weigh down the powerful prey, without becoming entangled himself, the hunter can then stick his hands in the bass's gills to obstruct breathing. Recovery of a suffocated giant lying prostrate on the floor of a sea forest posed a thorny problem until someone decided to attach an inflatable life jacket to the nylon line. When the gun is triggered, the life jacket springs to the surface as a marker for surface craft. Once the black bass hunter has his prey, he looks for enough friends on whom to pawn off four hundred pounds of fish meat.

For underwater hunters interested in less arduous activities the sea forests provide abalone. This giant of the snail family consists of a meaty white "foot" encased in a lead-colored shell up to a foot in diameter. Abalone will cover a submarine cliff like a coat of mail, their feet gripping tenaciously to the cliff. The abalone hunter uses a tire iron to pry his quarry from its vertical perch. The rubbery foot is tenderized with a wooden mallet and fried in butter, and the shell, which has a mother-of-pearl sheen, can be used as a decorative ashtray. (Indians in California preferred to embed the shells in the shoulder bone of a whale. Thus decorated, the bone served as a funeral bier.) California takes its abalone resource so seriously that out-of-state shipments are prohibited to conserve the supply.

The abundance and variety of life encountered in a sea forest are founded on the kelp's "biomass" capability. Biomass is the amount of living matter per unit of area. A kelp plant, with its multitude of fronds, injects far more living matter into a given area than the ocean's tiny current-driven plankton. Kelp concentrates marine life, whereas plankton, which drifts about the ocean in pasture-sized clumps, disperses life.

The key to this biomass capability is that kelp is the fastest growing plant on this planet and one of the largest and most prolific. This stature has been achieved without the aid of chemical fertilizers, pesticides, or agricultural extension services. Because the kelp's prime source of energy is photosynthesis, the fronds that bud from the holdfast virtually race to reach the sunlit ocean surface. They can grow two feet in a day and double their length in fourteen days. The holdfast, meanwhile, must expand its rootlike grip on the bottom to withstand the pull of the waves and of the floats that buoy up the fronds. This balancing act forces kelp to grow in rocky bottom areas, for the fronds would uproot the plant from a sand anchorage.

Once at the top, the frond creeps over the ocean surface to bask in the sun. The corrugated shape of its lanky blades increases sun exposure. These blades also filter and store iodine, potassium, and other mineral nutrients from the ocean. The thick brown canopy that results shuts off the young bottom fronds from life-nourishing sunlight. To overcome this blackout, the adult surface fronds pass down their energy to the young lower fronds in a process called translocation, a nutritional self-sacrifice that allows the frond to live only for about seven months. Then it shrivels up, sloughs off from the canopy, and drifts in to a beach, there to be despised by bathers.

The thick surface vegetation not only drives most other marine plant life from a kelp-dominated area but impedes the kelp's own reproductive capacity as well. Because germinating kelp spores must find a place on the bottom to which sunlight can penetrate, those that are able to survive and grow usually drift to the periphery of the forest, where the canopy is not so lush. A kelp plant emits a constant stream of seeds (up to seventy trillion annually) to ensure that enough will find a place to grow.

This capacity for vegetative and sexual reproduction makes kelp the biomass champion of the ocean. Thus a concentration of this seaweed becomes a forest inside the ocean, a splendid sanctuary for marine life, a submarine playground for divers, big-game hunting grounds for spear gunners, and bountiful fishing grounds for anglers, both commercial and sport. One day, on poking my head through the kelp canopy, I discovered another thriving human activity. An ungainly barge was lumbering along, its deck piled high with kelp.

The kelp industry emerged after a heated diplomatic exchange. In 1910 Germany enjoyed a world monopoly on potash deposits, an important fertilizer. When Germany replied sharply to an American accusation that potash prices were being rigged, the U.S. Congress authorized the Department of Agriculture to uncover potential domestic sources of the compound. That potash contains acetone, a critical element in ammunition, helped to spur the search. The ability of kelp blades to remove potassium, a prime base of potash, from the ocean qualified sea forests off southern California as a potential new potash source. A dozen prospective kelp-harvesting companies sprang up, many with no idea at all how to harvest kelp but with definite ideas on bilking eager investors. Southern Californian fishermen complained that kelp harvesting, however accomplished, would scatter fish communities, and beach residents grumbled that cut kelp would litter their front yards. Germany reacted to all this activity by becoming more flexible in potash negotiations, but World War I terminated this flexibility. The sea forests were immediately drafted into the war effort and served well by enabling DuPont to fill munition contracts for our allies as well as our own armed forces. Men in rowboats yanked the kelp from its holdfast, tug-of-war fashion. Kelp was then allowed to wash ashore, where burning reduced it to potash. The Hercules Powder Company mechanized this crude process by outfitting barges with cutter blades and harvesting the kelp like hay. The kelp was then fermented in large vats. In a year's time, thirty-five hundred tons of potash were recovered from three hundred five thousand tons of kelp. Although kelp harvesting did not realize the fears of fishermen and beach residents, its fermentation left an indelible impression on one visitor to the Hercules plant in San Diego. "There came galloping out to meet us, before we even got to the outpost, a smell that would cause women to faint and strong men to hesitate. It didn't smell like anything else in the world, but once smelled it is never forgotten," explained the visitor.

At the end of the war kelp harvesting slowed to a crawl, but a new era in prepared foods, premixed medicines, and synthetic products was dawning. Dampness was disintegrating aspirin, packaged ice cream, and other harbingers of the new era, and a chemical fastener or stabilizer was required. Kelco Company of San Diego, a survivor of the kelp depression, found that a particular compound in kelp endowed the fronds with a tensile strength that allowed them to withstand the constant wave surge. An extract from this compound, algin, proved to be' successful in keeping ice cream together without affecting its flavor, color, weight, or cost. Today algin suspends, stabilizes, gel-produces, and emulsifies laxatives, penicillin, candy, babies' rubber pants, and some three hundred other products. The sea forests off southern California thus insure the synthetic age from collapse.

Besides pioneering in ocean exploitation, the kelp industry has pioneered in its conservation. The industry has volunteered to pay increased fees to the California Fish and Game Department, which leases the forests as a property of the state, to underwrite enforcement of harvesting regulations. The mechanized barges that sweep through the kelp like hay reapers are allowed to cut to a depth of only four feet so that the forests can quickly regenerate. Because kelp has difficulty surviving in warm water and dies when the water temperature goes above seventy-five degrees, harvesting is restricted during critical warm spells.

The reproductive capacity of the kelp, the foresight of the industry, and the prized recreational allure of the forests would seem to preclude destruction. Yet for the last fifteen years the sea forests off southern California have been faced with just such a prospect. The kelp degeneration began in the late 1940's when harvesters found that they had to make longer and more costly runs to reach healthy kelp stands. By the late 1950's, the Palos Verdes forest off Los Angeles, which once embraced three square miles, was a virtual marine desert. The Point Loma forest off San Diego, originally six square miles in size, shriveled to a 0.6l-square-mile patch. In a visit to these once flourishing areas I found myself roaming through a ghost forest, strangely somnolent except for stray perch or a clutch of leafless, stringy fronds. Charles Darwin's century-old vision of chain destruction had become a reality. "I can only compare these great aquatic forests with the terrestrial ones in the intertropical regions," he noted in *The Voyage of the Bea-*

gle. "Yet if in any country a forest was destroyed, I do not believe nearly so many species of animals would perish as would here, from the destruction of the kelp. Amidst the leaves of this plant numerous species of fish live, which nowhere else could find food or shelter; with their destruction the many cormorants and other fishing birds, the otter, seals, and porpoises, would soon perish also. . . ."

Fishermen, along with skin divers and beach residents, blamed overzealous kelp harvesters for the recession. Kelp harvesters blamed a proliferation of coastal sewage outfalls. As in the case of the Florida red tide, an ocean poorly understood lends itself to heated exchanges born out of ignorance.

In 1958 the state of California initiated a five-year investigation into the kelp decline. Dr. Wheeler North then of Scripps Institution of Oceanography, a soft-spoken, well-tanned, scuba-diving ecologist, was appointed project officer. To scientific sea rangers kelp poses its own peculiar problems. Studying a kelp plant, Dr. North has noted, is like "studying a Sequoia tree." Seven full days are consumed in laying out a kelp plant on the beach and then studying, measuring, and analyzing the two-hundred-foot specimen. The fact that the kelp decline occurred off coastal cities led to suspicions that sewage outfalls were undermining the health of kelp with effluent, oil-field brine, soda ash, dyestuffs, starch acids, and other urban excretions. Suspended sewage particles floated about like dust in the dying forests. In the laboratory, however, Dr. Kenneth Clendenning of Scripps found that kelp actually flourished in sewage water.

Turbidity, the ability of suspended sewage particles to shroud life-nourishing sunlight, was also investigated. A verdict was suspended for lack of accurate scientific measurements.

While the kelp recession was baffling Dr. North's team of twenty investigators, a solution was becoming more urgent. Warm water is to kelp what drought is to hay.

Exceptionally warm summer waters were intensifying the recession. In an urgent search for clues, Dr. North began ranging through the kelp forests. With a lead air tank strapped on his back and rubbery black "wet" suit protecting him from the chilly water, the doctor resembled a hunchbacked seal. In one day he would take as many as six dives; in a year upward of two hundred. At first he seemed fated to uncover underwater hazards instead of helpful clues. One day a laconic blue shark appeared. Dr. North started to shoot to the surface but a companion diver, James Stewart, restrained him. The Scripps diving officer, whose right arm is scarred by a shark bite, motioned for stillness. "The shark then began investigating us," recalls Dr. North. "Its snout even bumped into my camera, but it drifted away as casually as it had appeared."

One day Dr. North's air supply waned and he started to the surface. A wave surge swept past, and suddenly he found himself anchored to the sea floor. A line from a buoy had looped around his air-tank controls. Another wave surge unraveled this ugly entanglement, and the doctor escaped an underwater hanging.

Another time, while in the cleft of a submarine canyon, Dr. North tried to turn on his reserve air supply. The controls failed to respond. He motioned to a companion diver, who yanked out his air-hose mouthpiece and permitted the doctor a hungry breath. The two then began climbing to the surface, sharing breaths from the single air tank. On land one hundred fifty feet may be only a short dash, but in the ocean depths it can be an exhausting journey. "The other diver was a better swimmer. Being half out of breath, I had trouble keeping pace," recalls Dr. North. He was virtually spent by the time he broke through the ocean surface. He later discovered that the controls on the tank, which he had borrowed, were incorrectly set.

After experiencing the trials of a sea ranger Dr. North finally uncovered a vital clue in a dying kelp forest. He observed only one creature in any abundance, the bottom-hugging sea urchin, which resembles a purple pincushion full of pins. The pins, which are spines, can puncture a man's flesh.

The presence of these urchins perplexed Dr. North. Equipped with five microscopic teeth, an urchin can set a kelp plant adrift by supping on its holdfast anchorage. One urchin would not pose much of a problem to a bountiful sea forest, but urchins, like locusts, move in "fronts" of as many as one hundred urchins per square yard. Only because these fronts move on at about a yard a day does a sea forest have a chance to regenerate. Yet Dr. North had observed sedentary urchins by the millions within the confines of a dying forest. It was as if a hundred cattle had been grazing on an acre of alfalfa. Urchins can survive for a year by supping on the tissues of their own reproductive organs, but their survival stamina did not entirely explain their populous presence. Were these urchins feeding on sewage particles and scum algae spawned by the sewage? As sewage-subsidized feeders, the sedentary urchins would deprive the kelp in the area of any chance to regenerate.

The aftermath of a shipwreck lent support to Dr. North's theory of unbalanced ecology. In 1957 the tanker *Tampico* was stranded off a rocky cove in Baja California, disgorging its cargo of refined oil. The oil spill spread over an area characterized by an abundance of urchins and an absence of kelp plants. In a year's time, however, the oil had apparently exterminated the urchins, thus liberating the regenerative power of the kelp.

Dr. North decided to experiment with urchin purges off southern California, but he lacked an agent of extermination. Shipwrecked oil tankers are hard to come by. Fur hunters had long since purged the cublike sea otter, the one major predator able to stomach the urchin's spiny exterior. France controls urchin populations by consuming urchin gonads as a delicacy, but the American palate is not yet prepared for them. Fencing them off from sea forests is ineffective because urchins can climb. One day Dr. North and a squad of scuba divers armed with hammers descended on an urchin-infested forest. Instead of smashing the urchins, the men surfaced with spines embedded in their hands.

While Dr. North was extracting the spines, a colleague, Dr. David Leighton, read that quicklime was being used on the eastern seaboard to exterminate starfish gorging on commercial oyster beds. In the laboratory quicklime proved just as effective on urchins. At the same time, perch, bass, crayfish, and kelp remained immune to it. Although susceptible to the tissue-burning properties of quicklime, abalone could withstand the low doses required to snuff out urchins.

In one experiment a dose of quicklime cleared urchins from a half acre of the Palos Verdes forest off Los Angeles. Three months later kelp fronds began wriggling up from new plants, but six months thereafter the new kelp colony had vanished. Dr. North's first quicklime purge had been frustrated by the ability of nearby urchins to scent young kelp. At about this time the project's skiff was stolen. "Who knows, maybe it was an urchin," mused Dr. North.

He then decided that an urchin purge over a wider area might prove more permanent, but by this time five years had passed, and the state of California had stopped financing the kelp investigation. Kelco agreed to provide the money and a kelp barge to sow the quicklime. Forty tons of quicklime descended like a snowfall on a five-acre area in the Point Loma forest. Urchins by the thousands perished, and kelp began to sprout. Then a curious thing happened. Neighboring urchins migrating toward the budding forest stopped short at its periphery. Dr. North concluded that the urchins were cooperating with his experiment but only because bottom drift kelp from the revived forest met their food needs. In March of 1964 twenty-seven more acres in the Point Loma forest were treated. In 1965 Kelco harvested the forest for the first time in seven years and collected eleven thousand tons of kelp. That is a great deal of emulsifier.

Today Dr. North, currently associate professor of environmental health engineering at the California Institute of Technology, colonizes marine deserts with kelp. Hearty kelp plants from a flourishing forest are severed at the holdfast, towed some five or ten miles by boat to a suitable rocky bottom, and anchored there by buoy. Spores from the transplanted kelp nurture a new forest. The fact that fish graze heavily on isolated strands of kelp requires transplanting many plants. In his latest project Dr. North will be towing in one hundred plants. Using another method of reforestation, Einar Anderson, Dr. North's research assistant, cultures kelp seedlings on nylon rope in the laboratory and then sets the rope on a rocky seabed, where the seedlings can take hold.

The combination of kelp's remarkable fecundity and man's ingenuity may well forecast new submarine forestation programs. Whereas coral beds require centuries and land forests, decades, transplanted sea forests will spring up in a year's time. Kelp's biomass ability to concentrate marine life may make such forestation programs a necessity. Some scientific admirers of kelp are excited about the possibility of modifying the plant's filtering ability to concentrate silver, gold, or precious vanadium salts that float in the ocean. (Interestingly enough, the state of New Jersey installs artificial seaweed in the form of plastic strands to temper offshore wave action and facilitate beach erosion control.) Meanwhile, sodium alginate in kelp is attracting medicinal as well as industrial interest. For some time researchers have been searching for a common substance that can purge strontium 90—harmful radioactive fallout—ingested by dairy cows and milk drinkers. Unfortunately, substances tested tend to purge body-building calcium as well. In tests with rats scientists at McGill University now find that sodium alginate discriminates between the two compounds and purges only strontium 90.

Such commercial versatility is only a preview of the richness of ocean flora. Most marine plants are just beginning to receive the scientific attention that kelp has lately come to enjoy. Yet the fact that the kelp decline in southern California is far from resolved suggests the difficulties future marine harvesters will face. Kelp harvesters note with chagrin the appearance of tiny urchins in the treated Point Loma forest. These are the offspring of the adult urchins that surround the forest and monopolize the drift kelp. The revived forest has thus served to foster an urchin population explosion, which could lead to a feverish cycle of liming.

A dying forest off La Jolla—which Dr. North explored as a boy—started to revive after a quicklime treatment. Then the red tide, the phenomenon that plagues the Florida Gulf Coast, tainted the La Jolla offshore. Young kelp plants, deprived of sunlight by the opaque waters, soon withered away.

A proliferation of coastal atomic power plants intensifies another kelp problem. Water used to cool reactors is discharged into the offshore. These copious discharges can raise surrounding ocean temperatures to kelp's survival threshold. To help ensure survival Dr. North is now studying use of a temperature-resistant kelp species found off Mexico.

The original catalyst of the kelp recession still remains an entrenched way of conducting civic business. Current laboratory and field tests sponsored by the U.S. Public Health Service and conducted by Dr. North, Dr. Leighton and Dr. Mary Clark show that urchins can absorb through their skin dissolved organic matter, especially amino acids, released by sewage discharges. Concentrations of amino acids and other dissolved materials in the marine environment are four to five times greater near outfalls. That sewage discharges may undercut the balance of marine nature with a nutritional as well as a toxic impact only adds to the problem of redressing this balance. Each day coastal cities in southern California discharge half a million gallons of sewage, or "fertilizer," into offshore waters. Other marine regimes have been subverted by such perverse nutrition. Excreta from duck farms drained into Long Island's Great South Bay, nourished oxygen-demanding algae blooms and snuffed out the local oyster industry. A glasslike fjord in Norway is periodically rendered opaque by a pungent green bloom fed by the sewage outfalls of Oslo.

The reaction to such carelessness is not encouraging. In championing the "receiving capacity" of the California offshore, a sanitary engineer noted, "All we may be doing is fertilizing the ocean." Today this cavalier attitude jeopardizes more than just the sea forests of southern California.

5.

The Haunted Dump

IN grade B crime movies members of the vice syndicate invariably outfit an upstart competitor with cement "shoes," row him out to sea, and gleefully push him overboard. This cinematic cliché is another testimonial to man's ageless belief in the ocean as the perfect haven for castoffs. We have been tossing, shoveling, squirting, leaking, spilling, sinking, draining, and dumping unwanted things into the ocean for centuries.

This carefree disposal—which supports an entire branch of knowledge, underwater archaeology—today nears floodtide proportions. An industrial society's most prominent product is wastes, wastes that grow in volume, variety, and toxicity and continually threaten to engulf us in gross ugliness and pestilence. As a solution to this pernicious productivity, the ocean is not only considered a handy dump but an economical one, fully capable of delousing—or at least concealing—mankind's tailings, with little or no assistance from man himself. We have been content just to deliver the stuff, and we have not been very particular about how we do it. "The pipe," observes one historian of technology, "marks the invention of the first sewage outfall." The ocean is considered —and quite properly—as a mixing process, which, stirred by powerful currents, is supposed to dilute the noxious and obnoxious. The ocean as a dump receives the supreme accolade of an industrial civilization: it is deemed a beneficial resource.

Yet it haunts us in an ever-increasing number of ways. In 1965 dead fish in large, stinking batches washed up on the beaches of Noordwijk, along Holland's North Sea shore. Observers spotted some beautiful blue crystals in the carnage, crystals later identified as copper sulfate, the same compound that was drafted to stem the Florida red tides. In water analysis the copper content of the coastal sea turned out to be five hundred times higher than normal. The Netherlands Institute for Fisheries Investigation discovered that large quantities of a copper compound had been dumped into the North Sea. Theoretically, based on the size of the sea, fifty-four hundred tons of any dumped substance would increase its presence in the water by only one millionth of a gram per liter (a gram equals one twenty-eighth of an ounce and a liter is a little more than a quart), but the currents in the mixing process that were to achieve this dilution fostered inshore concentration instead. Finally the currents began moving the deadly concentration away from Noordwijk . . . toward a coast rich in mussel beds. "Fortunately, north winds ultimately drove this contaminated water away from our coast," reports Dr. Pieter Korringa, Institute director.

As Holland's impromptu fish pogrom demonstrates, the ocean's vaunted mixing process is not always akin to that of a Waring Blender. It has its limits. To assume, as many do, that ocean currents run directly out to sea is but one way to challenge these limits. Minamata Bay is a ragged niche in the coast of Kyushu, a Japanese main island. A sweet abundance of fish and shellfish support the Bay's eleven fishing villages. Just inland lies

Minamata City, where a large chemical plant employs many of the city's forty thousand residents.

In 1953 a mystifying nerve disease made its appearance in Kyushu. A bright, agile teen-age boy discovered one day that he could no longer button his clothes or handle his chopsticks. Soon he began exhibiting infantile behavior, and his worried parents took him to a hospital. But doctors could not explain his sudden retardation, and the boy became a hopeless invalid at fourteen.

Another victim was a forty-two-year-old barber. When he did manage to get food into his mouth, the barber would pucker and smack his lips, and a rapid to-and-fro motion would seize his body. Gradually he deteriorated into an emaciated mute. Devoid of hearing and finger control, he still retained a single sense, that of pain. He, too, became a complete invalid.

An elderly fisherman was similarly stricken and had to call on his wife to bring chopsticks to his mouth. Within a week he could no longer walk. Within a month he was severely demented. Exiled to a hospital room, he growled, clawed his hands, and bared his teeth at visitors.

Between 1953 and 1960 one hundred and five cases of Minamata "disease," including seventeen in infants, occurred in the Minamata Bay area. Most ended fatally or in permanent, severe disability. "Minamata disease" began attracting worldwide medical attention. Doctors were baffled by its cause, much less its cure. Medical teams from the United States diligently examined the once-bright teen-ager, the barber, and the fisherman who bared his teeth. Encephalitis, toxic metals, and thiamine deficiency were all considered as possible causes, but all were ultimately rejected. Researchers were reduced to isolating living habits common to the victims of Minamata disease. Most lived in the fishing villages rather than the city. Many had cats as pets—cats that were often afflicted with the same disorientation that seized their masters. Some would even dash into the bay to drown.

The cats and their masters generally ate raw or cooked seafood caught daily in the bay. Sample Minamata Bay shellfish were forwarded to the National Institute of Health in Bethesda, Maryland, for exhaustive analysis. Although quite healthy in their own right, the shellfish were found to contain high concentrations of mercury, a silver-white element that has figured in many a poison plot. When these shellfish were fed to laboratory cats, the cats swiftly developed nervous disorders akin to Minamata disease.

Mercury's toxicity derives from its ability to penetrate the blood-brain barrier and disrupt the central nervous system. Mere inhalation of organic mercury compounds can prove fatal; in fact, most cases of organic mercury poisoning have involved farmers who were spreading fertilizers that contained mercury compounds. Where the Minamata shellfish were picking up their mercury temporarily perplexed investigators. Then it was noted that the large chemical plant in Minamata City had increased its production of vinyl chloride used in unbreakable high-fidelity phonograph records and other plastic products. Production had jumped from six thousand tons in 1955 to eighteen thousand in 1959. The compound was manufactured in a large reactor that contained a catalyst sequestered in small, amorphous pellets. After being processed the vinyl chloride was washed to rid it of impurities, including residues of the catalyst, which contained mercuric chloride. This washing process left the plant with volumes of impure water, and the answer to the problem of its disposal, typically enough, was to dump it into Minamata Bay. "Subsequent work has provided evidence that the responsible toxin for Minamata disease is associated with the discharge of mercury-containing effluent from the chemical factory," reported Dr. Leonard Kurland of the National Institute's neurological disease division.

The incidence of Minamata disease has decreased sharply since the chemical plant stopped using the bay as a handy dispose-all. Although fishermen and their families no longer wake up to find themselves unable to button their clothes, they have been cut off from their source of food and livelihood. The muds of Minamata Bay still contain high counts of mercury, and fishing was still prohibited in October 1966, according to Dr. Makio Uchida of Kumamoto University Medical School.

Dr. Leonard Kurland—now at Mayo Clinic—has cited the occurrence of Minamata disease "as an example of the need for careful study and control of possible new sources of industrial contamination of human seafood resources." This example served as a timely warning to the industrialists of Galveston Bay, near Houston, Texas. Here researchers found that plants along the bay were busily producing vinyl chloride and using mercuric chloride as a catalyst. The reason that no "Galveston disease" occurred was due less to specific precautions than to a chance difference in processing and washing methods. Specific precautions were promptly enacted to ensure adequately against any mercury leakage into the bay's rich oyster beds.

As the poison-carrying shellfish of Minamata Bay indicate, the mixing process of the ocean not only has its limits but its own idiosyncrasies. Its diluting effect can be effectively countermanded by shellfish who filter out and concentrate finely diluted compounds. This "ecological magnification," a necessary tool for life's survival in the dilute solution of the sea, has been corrupted by another heedless form of oceanic dumping. Dead fish, shellfish, and sea birds were recently washed up on a two-hundred-mile stretch of shoreline in the Pensacola, Florida, area. Investigators from the nearby Gulf Breeze Laboratory of the Bureau of Commercial Fisheries found in one dead loon a lethal concentration of dichloro-diphenyllrichlorethane, or DDT. Dolphins, mullet, and oysters had similarly high concentrations. Because no one was treating the Gulf of Mexico with DDT, investigators were stumped by its origin.

The source was finally traced to a measure taken to combat a troublesome beach problem. Dogflies were pestering the Pensacola beach trade, and beach crews were mobilized to disinfect the clumps of washed-up seaweed in which the dogflies lived. The disinfecting agent was the all-purpose DDT. In addition to permitting the DDT to wash into the Gulf on the tides, the crews cleaned their spray equipment in Gulf waters. The relatively modest amount of DDT used—130 pounds annually—was enough to transform oysters into living vials of poison. Oysters can store DDT at levels seventy thousand times greater than that of the surrounding sea solution. Like the shellfish in Minamata Bay, the gulf oysters were not themselves the victims of their own remarkable fixing ability. Although they are able to tolerate relatively high counts of DDT, oysters can also flush out these high counts over a period of time. More advanced members of the marine food chain (including man as well as seabirds and dolphins) can neither tolerate such high concentrations nor flush them out so readily. Pesticide residues which tend to collect in tissues and organs, such as the gonads, remain relatively stable except in periods of starvation. Thus higher members of the marine food chain can hoard pesticide residues until their survival is endangered. Even more ominous, one of the few ways that these residue levels are reduced is by passing them on in the reproductive process to the young. "This pesticide heritage," one scientist told me, "may be the twentieth century's version of original sin."

The Bermuda Petrel, a seabird whose contact with land is restricted to nesting rocks off Bermuda, is lately cursed by a high mortality rate at birth because of brittle egg shells. Dr. Charles Wurster, State University of New York at Stony Brook, now relates egg shell thinness to the Petrel's uptake of DDT residues on the oceanic food web. The Petrel now appears headed towards extinction.

Lower members of the marine food chain are by no means immune to the impact of pesticide runoff. Most pesticides are designed to kill insects; unfortunately, shellfish are closely related to insects. Accordingly, an unexpected by-product of mosquito-control programs has been the shrimp kills in bait pens along the Florida and Texas coasts. One such kill occurred recently in an estu-

ary responsible for sixty per cent of South Carolina's
shrimp catch. According to Mr. Philip Butler of the Gulf
Breeze Laboratory, the kill was associated with heavy
rains that washed lethal heptachlor used in fire-ant control programs into the estuary. Like shrimp, lobsters
and crabs do not require the concentrating ability of an
oyster to qualify for pesticide mortality.

The ability of pesticides to infiltrate the ocean regime
is sometimes staggering. Investigators from Johns Hopkins University found DDT residues in the fat and liver
of six penguins and one crabeater seal, animals that
inhabit an area presumably free of pest control programs—the Antarctic. Because polar penguins and seals
feed on nonmigratory fish and shellfish, it is theorized
that storm clouds pick up the residues over the conti-
nents and deposit them via millions of snowflakes.
(There are other indications that the ocean may emerge
as a vast settling basin for all civilization's fumes, locked
for transport into raindrops and snowflakes. Geochem-
ists at the California Institute of Technology report that
lead from auto exhausts rains into the North Pacific and
North Atlantic at fifty times the rate at which nature
introduced it in the past. According to Dr. Clair Patter-
son, this lead fallout—five hundred thousand tons annually—could ultimately subvert the ocean's mineral
nutrient balance and foster lead poisoning, which, like
mercury, affects the central nervous system. Lead is normally one of the rarest elements in the ocean.)

Some animals on land, like houseflies, can develop a
genetic resistence to pesticides, ostensibly by natural se-
lection; but what about fishes? Investigators at Gulf
Breeze exposed populations of sheepshead minnows to
DDT concentrations. The result was ninety per cent
mortality. In an unexpected reversal of the Darwinian
theory offspring of the surviving minnows, subsequently
exposed to DDT, proved much more sensitive than the
parent stock.

In the tissues of land animals pesticide residues within
the range of seven to ten parts per billion are not con-

sidered hazardous. "The existence of this level of pollution in estuarine waters is quite another matter," observes Mr. Philip Butler, who directs biological research at Gulf Breeze. "Within twenty-four hours, it will kill fifty to one hundred per cent of eight species of fish and crustacea that we have tested."

In little more than two decades DDT and other pesticides have purged malaria, yellow fever, and typhus from many areas of the world. This same potential for extermination in the ocean community makes the expanded use of pesticides—one hundred twenty-four million pounds annually in the United States alone—a perplexing problem, one in which we share a dual role as perpetrator and potential victim. "In the sea, there is the possibility of continuous recycling and concentration of the more stable pesticidal compounds until they pose a real threat to man's own welfare," declares Mr. Butler.

An even greater threat to human welfare may result from the indiscriminate introduction of radioactive material into the ocean solution. Dr. Roger Revelle, a past director of the Scripps Institution,* observes, "The most serious potential hazards to human beings from the introduction of radioactive products into the marine environment are those that may arise through the uptake of radio-isotopes by organisms used for human foods." Yet this very process is considered basic to the future of the nuclear power-plant industry. These plants will be generating huge amounts of radioactive wastes, and in plan after plan the ocean has been nominated as their logical receptacle, in some areas on the order of a ton or more a day. "If the sea is to be seriously considered as a dumping ground for any large fraction of the fission products that will be produced, it is urgently necessary to learn enough about [sea] processes to provide a basis for engineering estimates," notes Dr. Milner B. Schaefer, director of the Institute of Marine Resources, University of California.

* Now the director of the Harvard University Center of Population Studies.

Some engineering estimates have demonstrated a rather limited acquaintance with sea processes on the part of power-plant officials. Originally, the Atomic Energy Commission purchased thousands of old oil drums, stuffed them with broken test tubes, contaminated lab coats, dead guinea pigs, and radioactive waste, weighted them with cement, and then deposited them in the time-honored fashion of crime movies. Unfortunately, fishermen off the Atlantic coast began trawling up the drums in areas far from the dumping sites. Beachcombers on the Oregon coast even came across a washed-up drum marked "Atomic Energy Commission—DANGER—Radioactive Material." The AEC and the scientific world at large have only lately come to realize that underwater currents and internal waves can make the bottom of the ocean just as restless as the top. Contrary to past beliefs, scientists also find that life can exist at great ocean depths. This means that a creature of the deep who cannot read the AEC warnings may locate on the drums, leech out the radioactivity, and introduce it into the rapid-fire marine food web.

These embarrassing discoveries foster a new approach in radioactive disposal. England's Windscale Nuclear Works pipes fairly substantial amounts of radioactive wastes—about 50,000 curies per year—into the Irish Sea. Dispersion, not storage, becomes the trusted agent of safety. Although the Irish Sea has not been rendered "hot," the specter of ecological magnification is omnipresent. "Discharges result in enhanced radioactivity of the sea bed and of marine materials, such as seaweed and invertebrates, for some distance around the discharge point," cautions Dr. H. J. Dunster of the United Kingdom Atomic Energy Authority. The lettuce-leaf shape of purple laver, one type of seaweed, is especially adept at concentrating ruthenium-106. When Dr. Dunster observed people harvesting laver, he made inquiries and discovered that the seaweed is sold as a mash that resembles "dirty creamed spinach." Although laver is gener-

ally used as a condiment, Dr. Dunster found two Welsh-
men who consumed an average of 75 grams daily. As a
result of this preference for laver bread, Windscale disposal is restricted to low-activity wastes, which are partly
purified before discharge. "This is a good example of the
subtle secondary effects that have to be investigated
before dumping atomic wastes into the sea," notes Robert Cowen in *Frontiers of the Sea*.

The hot clams of the Marshall Islands certainly
deserve mention in this connection. Scientists were perplexed to discover high concentrations of the radioisotope Cobalt-60 in clams on this Western Pacific outpost.
Two years had passed since the area had been exposed
to radioactive fall-out. Furthermore, Cobalt-60 is not
produced by atomic fission. Where had the radioisotope
in the clam meat come from? "It must have been produced by the action of radiation on some chemical, presumably a stable cobalt isotope, naturally present in the
water," explained Dr. LaMont Cole of Cornell University. In other words, the ocean has the capability—ill-
defined and poorly understood—to react to nuclear
irradiation.

Within a few decades it is estimated that the world will
be faced with the disposal of one thousand tons of high-
level-waste fission products annually. The Western Pacific Ocean is vast, deep, and sparsely populated by man;
it affords a good test of the ultimate limit to the ocean's
ability to handle such waste products. In the U.S. atom
bomb tests in 1954 mixed fission products on the order
of a half ton were introduced into the upper layer of the
Western Pacific within a short time. "That this was near
the limit of safety is evidenced by the capture in adjacent areas of specimens of tunas and other fishes with
sufficient radioactivity to be doubtful for human consumption," observes Dr. Schaefer. The term "adjacent
areas" encompasses one million square miles. The same
fear served to prohibit natives of the Rongelap Islands
from enjoying coconut crabs, their favorite staple. The

prohibition remained in effect for five years while American food shipments subsidized the Rongelap diet. The Western Pacific thus had trouble handling a mere scrap of the world's future annual radioactive wasteload. The bottomless dump is daily becoming more and more of an illusion.

6.

The Haunted Dump Revisited

THE ocean dumping of industrial toxins, pesticides, sewage, and radioactive wastes haunts us because the marine food web absorbs and reincarnates these perilous discharges in the most apparently innocent forms. On the other hand, one commonly dumped substance plagues us precisely because the ocean has trouble absorbing it. The mother whose family returns home from a happy day at the beach only to track tar all over her deep-pile rugs can appreciate a statement by a prominent Scripps scientist, Dr. Claude ZoBell. "Oil pollution of rivers, streams, harbors, bays, beaches, and the open ocean has been increasing in frequency and intensity during the last century."

Dr. ZoBell, whose shoes and bare feet have, he admits, "become tarred, if not feathered" while inspecting beaches, finds that one class of animals is especially vulnerable to oil pollution.

Attracted by patches of oil floating on the water, many kinds of birds alight in search of food, or more likely they inadvertently swim into or emerge in oil after a dive. Their

plumage becomes fouled with oil, some of which may penetrate down under the feathers to the skin, thereby displacing
air which normally forms efficient insulation against cold.
Consequently, large numbers of birds freeze to death in the
winter and many more oil-fouled birds are unable to become
airborne. They may helplessly drift ashore to die of starvation, disease, or predation. Some oil-fouled birds lose their
buoyancy and sink.

A single oil spill in the North Sea fatally fouled more
than two hundred thousand waterfowl. Some ten thousand pelicans, gulls, grebes, loons, scoters, and swans
perished when an oil tanker, in a collision with another
ship off San Francisco, disgorged sixty-five thousand
barrels of crude oil. Over a two-year period oil pollution nearly decimated a colony of two hundred fifty
thousand auks on the Newfoundland coast.

Oily beaches have become a problem second only to
the meandering ones. Nantasket and other beaches within the cozy range of busy Boston Harbor average 21.8
pounds of oil per mile. One stretch of Cape Cod beach
alone boasts seventeen hundred fifty pounds of oil per
mile, which means plenty of tarred rugs in Provincetown. (One Provincetown resident remarked to me, "Hell,
we ought to drill those beaches for oil instead of sun-
bathing on them. We wouldn't even need a depletion
allowance.")

Well-lubricated beaches are now commonplace in
Byron's favorite marine haunt: "On the Mediterranean
seaboard practically all the beaches are soiled by the
petroleum refineries, and the sea bottom, which serves
as a food reserve for marine fauna, is rendered barren
by the same factors," reports the *Centre Scientifique de
Monaco*. When an unlucky sailor in the United States
Navy turned the wrong switch, some three thousand
gallons of diesel oil spilled out of the aircraft carrier
Shangri La. Ordinarily the ocean is big enough to hide
such errors, but the *Shangri La* happened to be anchored
but a half mile away from one of the Mediterranean's
most popular beach resorts—Cannes—at the height of the
holiday season. City officials, who had repeatedly asked
the Sixth Fleet not to anchor in Cannes Bay during the

summer season, dispatched a marshal by motorboat to serve a legal complaint against the carrier. Royal yachts were being smeared. Bright sails were soiled with oily spray. The advancing oil slick—which presented an uncertain fire hazard—began coating beaches and tourists alike with a sticky film. Visitors to Cannes were canceling their hotel reservations, leaving oil-stained hotel towels in their wake. The embarrassed Sixth Fleet swiftly mobilized an airlift, a helicopter bombardment, and an amphibious mop-up crew. The two-hundred-man work-party landed on the beach and dug a trench to intercept the oil spill's advance. Offshore, helicopters dumped two and half tons of silicone-treated sand on an advancing oil island and finally succeeded in sinking it. Meanwhile, the airlift hauled in clean sand from Naples. This air, land, and sea assault eventually mollified furious city officials. Hotels no longer contended with the problem of laundering tarred towels, and relieved Paris Travel agents reported that Cannes was once again oil-free.

Because most beach resorts cannot afford the Sixth Fleet on stand-by, the prohibitive expense of oil clean-ups has led to efforts to prevent oil pollution in the first place. The 1954 International Convention for the Prevention of the Pollution of the Sea by Oil, signed by a majority of the maritime nations, authorizes the establishment of oil-free zones one hundred miles seaward. Unfortunately, the anonymous nature of oil discharges frustrates the detection much less the prosecution of oil polluters, a fact readily verified by visiting any representative harbor. One can read signs that proclaim "Oil Emissions Punishable by Sentence and/or Fine" and then count any number of thick, spreading oil slicks. Scientists can sometimes tell if the slick has come from a bilge tank or a submarine seep, but identifying the particular tank or seep is generally beyond them.* This lack of methods for accurate detection comforts a captain faced with a special trip to sea just to flush out his fuel tanks or petroleum compartments. King-sized leaks from offshore

---

* The best chance for detection occurs when an oil spiller like the *Torrey Canyon* becomes trapped by a rock reef.

oil installations serve to compound the problem. Dr. Edward Deevey, head of the Environmental Section of the National Science Foundation notes, "Our continental shelves already carry 20,000 miles of pipeline, rusting and capable of releasing a disaster that would make the *Torrey Canyon* look like a grease spot." Dr. ZoBell reluctantly concludes, "The oil pollution of the sea is still largely an unsolved international legalistic, technologic, and economic problem." Effective tracing, identification, and control of oil pollution will yield only to exhaustive consideration. Dr. ZoBell's estimate applies with much the same force to the output of sewage outfalls, industrial effluent channels, pesticide runoffs, and radioactive waste pumps.

The dumping of more substantial trash into the ocean —such as old trolley cars and urban renewal rubble— occurs in much the same carefree and trusting manner as the disposal of liquid and semiliquid wastes. In California movie studios heave Roman villas, English castles, Western saloons, and other wornout movie sets into the ocean. The Los Angeles City Police Department contributes its annual haul of confiscated revolvers, brass knuckles, sawed-off shotguns, and bazookas. The ocean not only puts this four-ton armory out of sight but out of action as well. Firing pins quickly corrode, and such decomposition is cited as an example of the ocean's ability to "digest" debris, just as its size is supposed to dilute the output of sewage outfalls.

Such solid dumping would appear to pose a less pressing problem than oil spills and dogfly-control programs. This is generally true, at least as far as fish are concerned. Where man's activities in the sea are concerned it is a far different story. When the Air Force canceled the Navaho missile contract, North American Aviation Corporation was left holding a number of Navaho rocket engines. There is nothing quite so dead as last year's rocket engine and nothing quite so demanding of warehouse space. The Air Force advised North American to "deep-six" the space eaters. Today the one-story-high engines shelter small fish seeking refuge from sharks and other marine bullies. They also shred the nets of commercial fishermen who do not know they are supposed to be wary of underwater rocket engines. The use of the ocean as a junkyard proves equally exasperating to research vessels dragging expensively designed trawls.

The combination of an unanticipated current and restless debris can lead to other embarrassments. Recently the California state narcotics agency dumped "accumulated evidence" (i.e., confiscated narcotics) twelve miles off San Francisco. Just in case an enterprising dope pusher decided to waylay the cargo en route, the sea-going narcotics agents carried machine guns. About a week later seashell collectors on a San Francisco beach began picking up bottles labeled Metherdine, a powerful stimulant. More than 200 such bottles were found. Narcotics agent Matthew Conner was asked by the Associated Press if the bottles might be part of the recently dumped evidence. Mr. Conner sidestepped the question but did mention that the bottles might have been dumped by burglars. He added that the beach was being staked out to discourage prospective collectors of the exotic jetsam. Some months later a spokesman for the state narcotics agency told me that the source of the bottles had "never really been determined," but that burglars might have dumped them to be rid of damning evidence. When I asked if accumulated evidence was still deposited in the ocean, I was assured that there had been a change in procedure: the evidence is now incinerated.

Landward currents can foster situations far less amusing than drifting drug caches. One summer day in 1965 Galveston, Texas, was shaken by tremendous blasts, and a pall of smoke hung over the city. The cause of all this earth shaking was finally traced to a decision by a Texas chemical company to dump sixteen drums of sodium oxide residues twenty miles out in the Gulf of Mexico. "The barrels were dumped one at a time and then were shot with a 30–06 rifle to admit water and initiate an explosion, which was intended to sink the drum," reported Coast Guard investigators. Seven drums, on their unexpected return to shore, conveniently missed all ship traffic and exploded loudly but harmlessly on the spacious beaches of Galveston. Fortunately, this city had done a better job of preserving its beach buffer than other communities.

Such explosive results from ocean dumping—which would appear to fall into the freakish-accident category—already cloud the future of a major marine activity. Ever since a valiant German chemist tried—and failed—to pay off his country's World War I reparations by extracting gold from the ocean, the prospect of marine mining has dazzled the public imagination. The recovery of nodules, precipitated lumps of crude ore on the sea bed, has always been a more appealing approach to sea mining than straining the ocean. In either case no mine shafts would have to be sunk, explosives detonated, or mining towns constructed.

In 1961 the Collier Chemical and Development Company in Los Angeles decided to mine the 40-Mile Bank, a sea mount named for the distance it lies off San Diego. The bank was carpeted with nodules of phosphate. The depths involved—about one hundred feet—were within reach of a vacuumlike hydraulic dredge, guided by TV eyes. Although not so glamorous as gold, the nodules offered the prospect of substantial profits. In relying heavily on phosphate as a fertilizer, California's huge agriculture industry must import a supply all the way from Florida. Collier gladly paid the U.S. Department of the Interior one hundred thirty-seven thousand dollars to procure a lease on the 40-Mile Bank, but in a subsequent communication to the department the company said it was "shocked" to discover that "unexploded naval projectiles" littered the concession. The Navy promptly verified that the area had been used "Monday through Sunday" as a combination shooting gallery and dumping grounds. The Navy refused to guarantee that all its five-inch salvos and twenty-millimeter shells had exploded. After calling on ninety firms and determining that no economical system could detect live shells without retrieving them, Collier asked for a refund on its lease money. (The mining system that Collier planned to utilize is now dredging diamonds off South Africa, a country whose seabed has not yet been booby trapped by its navy.) Devising a marine mining system is hard enough without having to armorplate it.

The Interior Department refused Collier's demand for a refund, maintaining that the company should have been aware of naval activities in the area. The General Accounting Office overruled this decision. In a letter to me Frank Weitzel, acting Comptroller General, said, "We felt that there should have been prior affirmative disclosure of the existing hazards. Compare in this regard General Property Management Regulations with respect to the extreme care required in the decontamination of excess and surplus property incident to the management and disposal of same in order to prevent such properties becoming a hazard to the general public."

Because no detailed geological survey of the United States' continental shelf exists, the Interior Department has no way of knowing what other seabed resources are being jeopardized by dumping until someone's equipment snags, breaks, or explodes. About thirty miles off the North Carolina coast lie the Outer Banks, a favorite commercial fishing grounds, especially for scallops. Unfortunately, the fishermen have also dredged up death, for the area has long been used as a practice bombing range. One summer night Captain Edward Berry of the trawler *Geraldine* was hailed by the captain of *Snoopy*. Captain Doody reported that he was hauling aboard a huge bomb snagged in his nets. Berry requested that the *Snoopy* back off from the fishing area and radio when the bomb was clear of the net. When the *Snoopy* was about three hundred yards astern, Berry heard a "terrible blast that shook the whole area. I looked and the *Snoopy* was just gone." Berry could see sharks thrashing about in the light of flares dropped by Coast Guard rescue planes. Only four of the twelve crew members were rescued.

Polluting and despoiling the ocean hardly seems a civilized solution to the problem of waste disposal. Dr. Pieter Korringa, who identified the lovely lethal blue crystals that caused the Holland fish kill and who subsequently directed a United Nations study on ocean pollution, observes, "While there is no question of suppressing the use of the sea for disposal of wastes, we must decide how dumping can be done without turning many parts of the sea into man-made deserts." The ocean can quite properly save us from our wastes but only if dumping operations are charted, plotted, and predicted as carefully as shipping operations.

Such a critical capability is in short supply. The Committee on Oceanography for the National Academy of Sciences observes, "We lack both the engineering knowhow and the basic scientific background on the physical, chemical, and biological processes in the estuarine and coastal marine environments required to treat the problem [of marine pollution]."

Notes Dr. Deevey, "I am not comforted when I learn from the Public Health Service that the number of new compounds currently reaching the sea, whose ability to process them is uncertain, now approaches half a million."

To remedy such crippling ignorance the agency that had previously overlooked the dangerous implications of underwater currents is now sponsoring a pioneer study of sea processes. The study, commissioned by the Atomic Energy Commission and involving more than forty-two research projects, will be both expensive and time-consuming. It may conclude that present restrictions on radioactive disposal—based on conservative assumptions due to lack of precise knowledge—can be lowered with consequent economic savings. On the other hand, the study may find that existing restrictions are not conservative enough and that disposal of radioactive wastes will, in time, make nuclear power plants economically prohibitive.

Although not so dramatic as radioactivity nor so deliberately introduced into the ocean regime, pesticide runoff deserves the same careful and exhaustive consideration. Checking to see that coastal and river mosquito-control programs do not also wipe out shrimp poses obvious technical and political problems. Such monitoring, however, will ensure that our estuaries remain good shelters for more than thirty of our most important commercial species of fish and crustacea.

The extension of sewage outfalls farther and farther out to sea (one Los Angeles outfall extends five miles out) is becoming an increasingly expensive way of deterring inshore pollution, particularly when the specific catalysts of this pollution are poorly understood. As in the case of the AEC, less ignorance here may mean lower costs. An unsophisticated approach to the ocean can breed undue restrictions as well as mercury poisoning and radioactive tuna. Sanitary districts now discharging into the Southern California offshore are sponsoring a joint study of the environmental impact of their discharges. Some of these districts are learning to reuse effluent rather than dump it into the ocean; treated effluent is a cheaper source of water than the publicized desalinization of ocean water.

"Navigational hazard" is the prime limitation on the dumping of solid debris. The Army Corps of Engineers, in enforcing this limitation on our coastal waters, generally defines "hazard" as anything that sticks out of the water. This definition effectively jeopardizes our capability to operate below the surface, either directly or by remote control. An expanded definition of navigational hazard may crimp naval gunnery practice and rocket disposal; at the same time it will demonstrate a public awareness that there is more to the seabed than just starfish.

In time carefully planned ocean dumping may lead to profitable by-products other than underwater archaeology. The fish population in the North Sea off the Thames estuary is today double that of neighboring areas. Scientists now credit the city of London for such an impressive statistic. By dumping sewage into the Thames the city contributes some three thousand tons of phosphate annually to the nourishment of plankton pastures. (Biologist Romeo J. Mansueti credits the capital of the United States with doing the same for the striped-bass population in Chesapeake Bay.) In already rich sea areas such "superfertilization" may be destructive, as in the case of the kelp forests off southern California or the oyster beds off Long Island, but in barren or underproductive areas *carefully planned*, nutritious outfalls may not only be feasible but necessary. Dr. Joel Hedgpeth, a distinguished oceanographer and presently director of the Marine Science Center at Oregon State University, observes: "Massive withdrawals of living substances of the sea by man, without any thought of replacement, may not be feasible. We cannot take billions of dollars from the treasury without some sort of readjustment, yet we have taken billions of pounds of organic matter from the sea in a short time. If man expects to maintain his increasing numbers on the earth, he must give up his wasteful procedures of removing his remains and metabolic waste products from the cycle by sanitation processes that are essentially anti-ecological."

Dumped junk may prove just as beneficial to the sea regime as nutritious outfalls. In the 1930's a New Jersey sport-boat operator noted that surprisingly productive fishing often occurred off sunken shipwrecks and dumped auto hulks. Even though it neither rains nor snows down there, fish crave shelter. The ocean can seem to be an open prairie if a shark is on your tailfin. A handy porthole can mean salvation and a frustrated shark. The observant boat operator, Robert Pierpoint, deliberately dumped auto bodies and rubble into a barren seabed off Cape May, New Jersey. Fish were soon darting in and out of car trunks and nipping at the hooks of Pierpoint's delighted clients. The Cape May Fishing Preserve helped inspire a coastal chain of artificial fish reefs off California. Installed by the California State Fish and Game Department, these rock-rubble reefs feature catches of bass that run to seven per angler hour. When the fertilizing capabilities of sewage outfalls are combined with the shelter attraction of dumped debris, such reefs may realize the promise of sea farming and sea ranching.

Used wisely, the ocean as a dump may truly become a beneficial resource. Abused, it will continue to deteriorate into a haunted dump in which fish nets can be shredded into string, marine forests can be despoiled, and research vessels can be blasted into flotsam in an instant of time.

7.

The Wrecked Nurseries

SOME inhabitants of the ocean turn landward when the time to spawn arrives. Mullet and tarpon spawn in the warm, quiet inlets behind barrier beaches. Other fish go far beyond the coastline, penetrating hundreds, even thousands, of miles inland. They swim intently against the current of an ocean-bound river, hurdling rocks and rapids, dodging eels and the swift claws of bears, finally coming to rest in green-shaded mountain streams where they were born and where they have come to give birth. Such gallant fish are called anadromous—upward running.

Anadromous fish include some of mankind's most prized species: shad, striped bass, alewife, salmon, and Edward the II's royal fish, the caviar-bearing sturgeon. Over the centuries their arrival from the ocean has stirred great commotion and activity. Indian tribes suffering stomach pangs worshiped the return of the "fish people" who feasted and danced beneath the sea. Today fishing fleets, blessed from the pulpit, flock to river mouths in Oregon, Alaska, Ireland, Scotland, and Norway to greet schools of salmon that redden the water. Business executives and truck drivers temporarily desert their families and while away preciously hoarded vacation hours in casting feathery lures into wilderness rivers. School children descend on river banks and cheer when a silvery twisting form leaps out of the river and clears a small waterfall. Scientists eagerly troop from laboratories to mountain streams to observe a fish deposit a million tiny transparent eggs. Housewives forsake red meat for poached salmon garnished with water cress and baked shad basted in butter and lemon juice.

Yet in many parts of the world this happy commotion is only a memory, perpetuated by old net fishermen on relief and academic devotees of regional history. Whether the stir of the fishing fleets, the urban sportsmen, the school children, the scientists, and the housewives will become a world-wide memory depends on an exacting campaign to save the river nurseries of the anadromous fish.

The Aroostook River rises in two mountain lakes in northern Maine. It courses through pine woodlands, draining small streams and lakes called Limestone, Caribou, Squapan, and Mooseleuk. After drawing off some one hundred fifty-six rain-rich lakes and streams the Aroostook spills into the St. John River, across the Canadian border. Reinforced by the Aroostook, the St. John moves across the province of New Brunswick to pour into the Atlantic Ocean by way of the tide-wracked Bay of Fundy.

The Aroostook River, some two hundred miles inland, more than five hundred feet above sea level, and but one hundred miles long, has historically attracted alewife, shad, and striped bass from the depths of the ocean. Two thousand miles away, in the chilly waters off Greenland, Atlantic salmon graze in rich sea pastures and dodge icebergs and killer whales, whose stomachs can digest twenty salmon at a time. When spawning time approaches, the salmon, robust, silver-coated, and black-specked, turn south toward Newfoundland and

Nova Scotia, where they are joined by others, fat from feeding. At the craggy tip of Nova Scotia thousands of salmon traditionally branch off from the pack, turn into the Bay of Fundy, and search out the brackish mouth of the St. John. After journeying up St. John, the salmon glide into deep pools along the Aroostook. Insulated from the summer sun, they wait patiently for their eggs to ripen. Their silvery coats have darkened to a reddish hue, and they have lost about forty per cent of their body weight. From a blue world of whales, squalls, and harsh ocean pressures, they have slipped into a green world of beaver, trout, pine needles, and radiating ripples.

When fall arrives, the salmon forsake the deep pools for the gravel beds of shallow streams. Not all automatically enter the first stream encountered on the Aroostook mainstem. Each salmon may pass up five, ten, or twenty streams before casually making a left or right turn. Where the salmon turns is where it was born. The female will then scratch out a five-inch crib in the gravel with her tailfin and deposit a number of her eggs. A waiting male, his back arched, his mouth strained open, instantly disgorges a white cloud of milt, which penetrates the eggs, fertilizes them, and then dissolves in the water of the stream. The female moves upstream to fashion another crib, the scratched-up gravel settling over the crib just fertilized. This crib making may last as long as a week, and many thousands of eggs may be laid by one female. The spent salmon depart quickly, hurrying to reach the Atlantic before the Aroostook and the St. John ice over.

Shielded from freezing temperatures, aerated by stream currents, nourished by the yolk sac, the salmon eggs hatch into fingerlings in the spring. Supping on a thousand insects, the fingerling coasts along the river current, tailfin first, and backs into the Atlantic. The young salmon then makes its way to the Greenland offshore to congregate with its parents and its brethren from the coastal rivers of Iceland, Norway, Ireland, and

Scotland. It is a cosmopolitan group and a very elite one. Out of every three thousand eggs laid approximately one makes it to the adult stage. After about five years of chasing down tiny red shrimp, the young grow into robust fifty-pound specimens of marine vitality. They are now prepared to lose almost half their body weight in their journey to the headwaters of the Aroostook where they will dig their own cribs in the gravel.

In providing the Atlantic salmon with more than seventy miles of choice spawning grounds, the Aroostook River system has supplied the entire New England region with a food resource of incomparable value. No tilled fields, fertilizers, sheep dogs, or ocean trawlers are required to harvest salmon. The salmon take care of the growth process in the ocean and then return to the very doorstep of the potential consumer and the eager canner. Describing how the enthusiastic Tobique Indians greeted the salmon, Williamson's *History of the State of Maine* reports:

> Fish were caught by hook and line, by entangling them in weirs, by dipping with scoop-nets, or by striking them with spears. Fish lines and nets were constructed of deer's sinews, the bark of trees, or tough grass, spun into threads between the hands and teeth; the hooks were bone grated to a point and bearded. Many Indian weirs were constructed of large stones.

Through the night the Indians pursued the sea salmon. As one anonymous white man observed, "In the night it is possible to paddle quietly along the stream with a flambeau burning in the bow. Then the sharp eyes of the men in the boat detect a salmon in the bottom of the stream. A quick thrust with a spear and the salmon is in the boat."

By 1894 a writer in the *Maine Sportsman* was extolling the fecundity of the Aroostook salmon to the white man. "It is the opinion of the fish commissioners, both of Canada and the United States, that the Aroostook waters are for the propagation of salmon, equal to any waters on the continent . . . thousands of salmon ascend the river every year." The Bangor and Aroostook Railroad Company, publishers of "A Big Game and Fishing Guide to Northeastern Maine," persuaded Boston bankers and New York merchants to travel to the "Haunts of the Hunted." After flicking orange, red, and green lures into the Aroostook the traveling sportsmen returned home with salmon steaks fit for watercress, endives, and lemon juice.

Today the Aroostook River is one of many places in the world in which the salmon run is largely a memory. The salmon who could buck upstream currents, evade eels, leap small water falls, hurdle rapids, and travel the North Atlantic has finally met his match in man's carelessness. Some seventy dams straddle the Aroostook River and its tributaries. In ushering northeastern Maine into the twentieth century, these dams have been allowed to choke off the salmon runs. Although they will try leap after vain leap, salmon just cannot clear dams that lack fish passageways. Gripped by an instinct that permits them to spawn only in their parent stream, the salmon will finally starve to death in the dam millrace with millions of eggs still inside their withered bodies.

Even a dam provided with a passageway means that the salmon's troubles have only just begun. The backed-up waters behind the dam may demolish its sense of direction by diluting the strength of the current. More seriously, the waters may flood out his shady pool and spawning grounds. The salmon who does find a likely pool may see it shrink into a stagnant puddle, as the waters that generally supply it are abruptly impounded behind an upstream dam. Besides stranding adult salmon, these upstream dams can lay bare the shallow gravel spawning grounds. If shady pools and wet cribs are still available, the salmon may finally be able to lay their eggs and return to the Atlantic, pending downstream dam construction, but if an upstream dam suddenly releases its hoarded waters to power a log drive the roaring torrent may sweep away the salmon cribs in a matter of seconds.

If the eggs manage to hatch, the fingerlings have a shot at survival in the Aroostook. The first test is often an irrigation diversion. Because fingerlings are inexperienced in distinguishing river from irrigation currents, they may wind up in a farm field instead of the Atlantic. If they do survive dams and diversions, they must then be able to stomach the sewage, the potato starches and the textile wastes that poison the waters, coat the gravel with greasy silt, and absorb the river oxygen. If the sewage outfalls do not prove potent enough, a method employed to expedite log drives very probably will. Bulldozers used to straighten out the course of a river or stream also wipe out any remaining indications that "the Aroostook waters are for the propagation of salmon, equal to any waters on the continent."

In 1965, before a Congressional hearing, Roland Speers of the Maine Inland Fisheries and Game Department, totaled up the toll of industrialization on the Aroostook and other salmon rivers of Maine. "We have ascertained that regular runs of salmon were once found in at least 33 rivers. There are regular runs in only six today." These runs have been maintained largely by artificial stocking, the limits of which are underlined by the fact that the Maine coast catch of salmon declined from one hundred fifty thousand pounds in 1889 to fewer than one thousand by 1950. Commercial fishing has almost entirely ceased. Sport fishing is an expensive excursion into nostalgia. In 1962 sportsmen, equipped with the latest Abercrombie and Fitch breakthroughs in colored lures and glass rods, landed a total of four hundred five Atlantic salmon. (This was considered a good year; in 1950 eighty-two were landed.) If two thousand sportsmen, a conservative figure, now indulge in what is called Maine salmon fishing, it means that five men are required to land exactly one salmon.

Today almost every major river on the Atlantic seaboard, from the Aroostook in Maine to the St. Johns in Florida, is saddled with dams and sewage outfalls, as evidenced in the catch statistics on other anadromous fish. In 1897 some 1.2 million pounds of sturgeon was landed in the states of New Jersey and New York. The New World gorged on the black eggs of this sluggish bottom creature, as children bounced its rubberlike snout on waterfront streets. In 1961 twenty-five thousand pounds was landed and few children even remembered what the nose of a sturgeon looked like. In 1897 forty-nine million pounds of blue-shaded shad was landed between Maine and Florida. Much of this catch was placed on oak planks, basted in butter, barbecued, and consumed right off the plank in a tradition nurtured by Thomas Jefferson. Today's shad catch is one sixth the total of the 1897 catch.

In the Old World the suppression of the anadromous fish proceeds in the same haphazard but all too thorough manner. Fishermen on England's River Tees caught eight thousand pounds of salmon in 1900; in the 1920's, three thousand pounds; in 1937, twenty-three; now, as on the Aroostook, virtually none. A new and deadly tributary, twelve million gallons of daily sewage, empties into the River Tees. On the Volga dams and pollution endanger the source of Russia's great caviar industry and help spur that country's massive move into the high seas fishery. To sustain its historic caviar industry, Russia loads caviar-bearing sturgeon aboard river boats to bypass slime-covered migration routes. Similarly, the Rhine no longer boasts its salmon.

The nonarrival of anadromous runs stirs a different but equally frenzied sort of activity. On the Atlantic seaboard sport and commercial fishing lobbies alternately persuade state legislatures to restrict one another's fishing on diminished stocks. By the 1854 Treaty of Medicine Creek the Puget Sound Indians of the Northwest gave up eleven million acres of land for about four cents an acre and "the right of taking fish, at all usual and accustomed grounds and stations, in common with all citizens of the territory." Today tribal members are jailed for exercising this right because of the need for conserving diminished salmon resources. "Children in this area don't play cowboys and Indians anymore," observed comedian Dick Gregory, an Indian sympathizer, "they play game wardens and Indians."

In addition to dams, irrigation diversions, and industrial wastes, the remaining anadromous fish contend with more modern hazards. In 1963 Consolidated Edison proudly opened a nuclear power station at Indian Point, along New York's Hudson River. Subsequent reports that a large number of crows were circling a dump near the new power station brought Dominick Pirone, consulting biologist to the Long Island League of Saltwater Sportsmen, to Indian Point. The power station sits alongside the spawning grounds of the striped bass, the gallant fish with which League members happily tussle in the Atlantic surf. As Pirone neared the dump, an odor of decay assailed his nostrils. Inside, bulldozers were shoving dead bass into heaps twelve feet high —stinking heaps that were being treated with lime to hasten their decomposition. Meanwhile, a run of trucks was dumping new batches of dead bass. Pirone followed the trucks and wound up at the Indian Point power station. He walked out on its dock. Below him, intake pipes cycled Hudson River water through the nuclear facility to cool its generator. Said Pirone, "I saw and smelled some 10,000 dead and dying fish under the dock."

The water that was cooling the generator was returned to the Hudson at temperatures seven degrees higher than normal. This warm water was enough to attract spawning bass under the dock, where they were trapped, began gorging on each other, and finally suffocated in the crowded waters. The intake pipes sucked the bass up into wire baskets for ultimate disposal in the dump marked by the circling crows. The simple placement of a fine mesh screen around the dock terminated this ugly chain of events, but only after an estimated two million bass wound up in the dump instead of in the Atlantic surf.

It would be heartening if the placement of a modest screen would suffice to save the river nurseries of all anadromous fish. But in reducing them to the level of industrial gutters, our society has placed such forthright solutions well out of reach. To be fully effective any program designed to preserve anadromous fish from extinction in the twentieth century must encompass the entire environment of the fish, from the international waters of the open ocean to the headwaters of mountain streams. Every human activity along this vast range, from fishing to waste disposal to water storage, must meet the breathing, feeding, and spawning requirements of the fish. Wherever these requirements clash with human activity, it would have to cease or a duplicate environment for the fish be created. A program of anadromous conservation thus runs up against every conceivable political and economic obstacle in modern life.

Yet just such a complicated program has succeeded on the most unlikely of rivers. The Columbia is really not a river anymore. More than a dozen major dams, including fifty-story-high Grand Coulee, have chopped up the mighty river into a chain of giant storage ponds at a cost of five billion dollars. Waterfalls as well as streams have been drowned. The dams, a host of sewage outfalls, irrigation diversions, logging runs, gravel-recovery operations, and river marinas all combine to make the Columbia River system the most highly developed water resource in the world—one seemingly impervious to the destiny of a salmon bearing thousands of eggs. That the salmon native to the Columbia—called king in respect for its occasional one-hundred-pound size—spawns but once would appear to hasten its extinction. Spawning is synonymous with death for the king; corpses of the spent adults float above the cribs of the young.

About one hundred forty miles after entering the

wide mouth of the Columbia, a king intent on fatal
spawning encounters sixty-five-foot Bonneville Dam. Instead of perishing in the millrace some five hundred
miles away from its parent stream, the king heads toward an area of the dam that, according to biologist
Brian Curtis, resembles "the imperial stairway of the
Fontainebleau Palace." Each "stair" consists of a pond
which permits the salmon to climb Bonneville at their
leisure. Instead of fish ladders, other dams may provide
fish locks, which, like boat locks, stand ready to elevate
the fish to a new water level. After a number of such
elevated assists, it can glide into a deep pool whose
coolness is maintained by a regulated flow from upstream dams. After a short summer residence here the
salmon proceeds to its parent stream, readied for occu-
pancy by bulldozers that clear away log jams and boulder barriers. If such careful stream clearance is not possible, a nearby stream diversion ushers the salmon into
an artificial pond. Here a biologist will yank out a sixty-
pound salmon, slice open its belly, and scrape out a
batch of eggs into a pail. A fellow biologist will squirt
milt into the pail by squeezing the underside of a male
salmon. Fertilized salmon eggs are then dumped into
an incubator pond. The adult salmon are ground into
meal and later served to the fingerlings that hatch from
the eggs, fingerlings that are then released into the
Columbia to join their stream-born counterparts bound
for the Pacific. Screens on irrigation diversions ensure
that the journey does not dead-end in a beet field. Fine
plastic nets set upstream of dams catch the fingerlings
before they can pass into dam turbines. The netted fingerlings are pumped or trucked to a point below the
dam spillway. One potential obstacle still remains
before they can glide into the Northern Pacific and
cruise past adults bound for the ladders of Bonneville:
sewage outfalls. Rigorous monitoring of waste discharges, including the radioactive residues of the Han-
ford Atomic Energy Reservation, takes care of this
obstacle.

On the Columbia man has become actively involved in the spawning and nursing cycle of the salmon. The technology of participation is extensive—twenty-one hatcheries, twenty-two major fishways, more than six hundred screened irrigation diversions, and some seventeen hundred miles of carefully cleared stream bed. It is also costly. To detour fifteen million fingerlings around Kelly Canyon Dam by aerated truck each year costs a million dollars. The price tag on the imperial stairways at Bonneville is six million. Since 1949 some forty million dollars has been expended on salmon chaperonage. Yet the prodigious bounty of the salmon serves to justify the expense. Each year some seventeen million pounds of Columbia salmon are caught. Although far below the record forty-nine million pounds of 1911, this catch still suffices to support a fishery valued at twenty million dollars annually. In the space of two years the cash value of the Columbia salmon run equals the money spent on perpetuating the run over the last fifteen years.

Despite such ample economic justification, neither of the three Columbia basin states—Washington, Oregon, and Idaho—could have mustered the required financial and political resources. What is officially called the Columbia River Fishery Development Program became possible only because river development is planned on a regional basis and largely financed and co-ordinated at the Federal level. The dam builders—the Corps of Engineers—and the salmon guardians—the Bureau of Commercial Fisheries—thus work together to integrate, rather than segregate, salmon survival from river development. This approach treats the anadromous fish as it should be treated—as a national resource. Since 1948 the state of Maine has mustered some four hundred thousand dollars to resurrect the glory of its thirty-three salmon river runs. This commendable, albeit totally inadequate, gesture is continually jeopardized by local decisions to build a cheap outfall or a barrier dam. A thirty-thousand-dollar project to erect a critical fishway on the Aroostook has been stymied by the elaborate dam plans of a local utility. As long as the fate of the Atlantic salmon rests in the hands of village councilmen and utility executives, the entire eastern seaboard will be denied their recreational, nutritional, and commercial value.

The survival of the Columbia River salmon compared with the continued plight of Maine salmon inspired the Congress in 1965 to pass a five-year, twenty-five million dollar program of anadromous conservation. Coupled with the Federal water-pollution control program and new advances in anadromous conservation, this program could "double or even triple the catch of anadromous fish," as the director of the Bureau of Commercial Fisheries, Donald McKernan,* predicted before the Congress. The high cost of artificial propagation is encouraging the Bureau to return this responsibility to the salmon themselves. Concrete channels akin to flood-control channels are being grooved in the wilderness, coated with gravel, filled with water, and connected with salmon rivers to serve as artificial nurseries. Going one step farther, scientists are seeking to divert salmon from parent streams which have been badly mauled to more suitable locations. Dr. A. D. Hasler of the University of Wisconsin feels that stream odors, not eyesight or some deep instinct, guides a salmon to the stream of his birth. Salmon who have their noses plugged with cotton or their olfactory nerves severed tend to miss the correct stream turn. If stream odors can be reconstituted in the laboratory and emplaced in other streams at will, man may be able to direct salmon traffic as safely and efficiently as a policeman at a downtown intersection.

Such promising developments come at a most critical time. Man-shaped rivers like the Columbia are becoming the rule rather than the exception. The conservation of anadromous fish, like any other form of conservation, flourishes best on a preventive rather than

*Now Special Assistant to the Secretary of State for Fisheries and Wildlife.

disaster basis, and this means ranking it on a planning par with dams and power plants.

In protesting Con Edison's plans to build the Storm King nuclear power plant beside the spawning grounds of the Hudson striped bass, Robert Boyle, conservation editor for *Sports Illustrated*, remarked, "You do not build a power plant on top of a spawning bed of an irreplaceable fish resource. I would no more think of licensing a plant for that area than I would of slaughtering sheep in my living room. It is just not the place."

The ability of giant power plants to warm rivers now menaces the millions spent on protecting the Columbia salmon. "Examination of water temperature trends in the Columbia Basin indicates that conditions for salmonids are approaching critical levels in the hot summer months," observes Dr. Stanley Cain, Assistant Secretary of the Interior. "Further impoundments of river-run hydro developments will expose additional masses of water to solar heating and push temperature levels even higher." Heat-drugged salmon are more susceptible to disease and predators alike. The government agency which licenses nuclear power plants has chosen to ignore their fish-drugging potential, as highlighted in the following testimony given at a recent Congressional hearing:

Congressman John Dingell (Michigan-Dem.). Assuming as a matter of fact that you were to find that a project you were licensing was going to raise the temperature of a major river by ten degrees, and this was going to have an enormously destructive effect on, let's say, a major salmon and trout stream, would the Atomic Energy Commission go ahead then and license that plant, in spite of that fact?

Harold Price (Director of Regulation, Atomic Energy Commission). Under the present law, I don't believe we could deny the license for that reason.

The AEC's determination not to enforce thermal as well as radiological regulations is more than just a case of strict legal protocol. Explained Mr. Price, "It [thermal regulation] would impose a burden on the nuclear industry that is not imposed on the conventional power plants." The salmon thus become the pawn in a struggle between two competing power industries. Recommendations by the Fish and Wildlife Service for thermal precautions at eleven nuclear power-plant installations have been ignored by the AEC. (Because of the cost of cooling off power-plant water—five million dollars for a modest plant alone—the Service recommends that cold waters from upstream dams be released periodically.)

Although the AEC would conceal thermal pollution behind legal hairsplitting, private power utilities occasionally resort to a different tactic. Congressman Richard Ottinger (New York-Dem.) describes Con Edison's reaction to the striped bass kill at its Indian Point installation:

> The story of the Indian Point fishkill is strangely obscure. There are reports of truckloads of fish carted away secretly; fish graveyards limed to hasten the destruction of evidence and guarded by Burns' detectives to prevent witnesses' access to see the size of the kill. There are stories of pictures suppressed by State officials and State employees pressured into silence.

It took a Dominick Pirone to pierce such calculated obscurantism.

Anadromous programs that manage to keep power plants in line can still be jeopardized by fishermen from adjoining states or nations who decimate fish stocks on the open sea. The problem of anadromous conservation thus becomes enmeshed in an even more demanding one to be discussed later in the book—overfishing.

Yet the bounty of the anadromous fish still justifies the preservation of its river nurseries. Dams need not be torn down, power plants dismantled, outfalls corked, and log drives stilled. These activities need only be blended into the natural world they exist in and depend on. A natural event of grand proportions is not all that is at stake. If we shut off the salmon, the shad, the striped bass, and the sturgeon from their nurseries, we will shut ourselves off from a food source of unparalleled value. The absence of salmon steaks and baked shad in the midst of our present agricultural affluence may go unnoticed, but to future generations faced with feeding many more mouths it would seem senseless. Ominously enough, anadromous fish are not alone in being evicted from our nurseries.

8.

Burial of an Estuary

THE rivers and the oceans of the world collide in surprisingly calm havens called estuaries. Some estuaries occur on a grand scale, deep, clear blue and grooved between glacial mountains, like the fjords of Norway or Puget Sound. Others are bustling harbors, like New York's Upper Bay. Most, however, appear rather unremarkable places, clogged with marsh grass, bottomed with mud, split by a maze of channels and beset with mosquitos and muggy odors. They exist on the treasured seashore but rarely rate mention in summer tour guides. These forsaken estuaries are among the most productive areas in the world.

Dr. Eugene Odum, a noted ecologist at the University of Georgia, is also the most devoted admirer of salt marshes and estuaries since Sidney Lanier. Dr. Odum has studied the fertility and natural productivity of jungles, rain forests, the open sea, and river valleys. He has also investigated the artificial productivity of farmland. His desire to measure the productivity of an estuarine area led him to Sapelo Sound, a rambling niche in the Georgia coastline. Based in large part on his studies of that water, Dr. Odum finds that estuaries are twenty times as productive as the open sea, seven times as productive as an alfalfa field, and twice as productive as a corn field.

Such enormous productivity, obtained without artificial fertilizers and the counsel of professors of argiculture, seems most incompatible with the afflicted nature of an estuary. "Tolerant plains, that suffer the sea and the rains and the sun," observed Lanier a century ago. Mud flats and marshes are alternately drowned by salty tides, drenched by sweet rains, and dried by the sun. The estuary waters are endowed with a half-caste character referred to as brackish.

Yet an estuary's shallow, sprawling nature provides a maximum of exposure to energy-giving sunlight, both for bottom-dwelling and surface organisms. Tidal flows and river currents circulate a rich supply of nutrients to be fixed by sun-powered photoplankton and marsh grass. This circulation also serves to retain many of the products of death and decay in the estuary, thus fostering a rapid turnover of nutrients. Here the rooted plants of the land and the drifting plants of the sea can flourish together, complementing one another's growth.

Such prime fertility supports an abundant marine community. Beneath the surface of these brackish waters beat the gills of innumerable ocean visitors: tarpon, snook, mullet, menhaden, and spotted trout. The estuary is as vital to these visitors as it is to the creatures who spend their whole lives in it. Many fish come to drop eggs that adhere to pebbles or vegetation below the surface, there to hatch into the richness of the tidal flux. The larva of clams and scallops cling to stalks of marsh grass and sup on mud algae. So do shrimp and killifish. The quiet, modest estuary is, in reality, a powerful biological engine driven by currents, the sun, land drainage and the tide-nudging moon.

For some marine creatures the estuary's richness is such that they move little or not at all. Minute diatoms swirling about in the tidal flux may suddenly find themselves caught in the mucus on the gills of a bottom creature which pumps eight gallons of estuarine water through its system every hour. The nutrients extracted by this pumping action enables the creature to secrete its own armor of hard white shell, inside which is nurtured a soft core highly prized by man. This creature is the oyster. From the sky above descends another spectrum of marine life, the shorebirds and waterfowl. "Whistling swans play hopscotch across the Great Lakes every fall to enjoy the wild celery in Chesapeake Bay," observes Dr. Alfred Etter. "The teeming life of coastline mudflats provides the energy for godwits, curlews, sandpipers and plovers to appear on the Great Plains a few days later, hungry for grasshoppers."

There are two prime reasons why the world's fishing industry focuses on coastal waters: (1) their convenience and (2) the fact that estuaries make the coastal waters rich fishing grounds. More than thirty of the United States' most important commercial species of fish, mollusks, and crustacea spend a part or all of their lives in an estuary. It is a spawning grounds, a nursing grounds, a feeding grounds, and a place to live. Two small estuary lagoons in Rhode Island—less than four square miles in size—contribute twenty-five per cent of the annual catch to the region's flounder fishery. The South Atlantic and Gulf coasts, from Cape Hatteras to the Mexican border, are fringed with lagoons, inlets, and bays. According to Seton Thompson of the Fish and Wildlife Service this almost continuous estuarine area is responsible for a coastal fishery that harvests more than a billion pounds of fish annually worth more than one hundred million dollars, including shrimp, America's most valuable commercial crop. More than forty thousand fishermen and twenty thousand workers in allied shore establishments are involved in this harvest.

Dr. Odum feels that an estuary's ability to nurture such a fishery is only a preview of its ultimate usefulness to man. Our exploitation of the land has generally been based on a system of cultivation: intensively grooming land to support one-crop or one-animal economies. Dr. Odum feels that the estuary's high natural productivity rate precludes the need for intensive cultivation efforts.

He considers "utilization" the key word. Instead of re-claiming salt marshes for use as lettuce fields, man should learn how to preserve, enhance, and share in its natural productivity. In the same manner, instead of transforming estuaries into farms, man's efforts should be directed to uncovering the food value of all estuarine creatures. Cultivation entails expensive projects of change; utilization merely requires knowledge.

Fish and Dr. Odum thoroughly appreciate the natural values of an estuary. Yet these very values are jeopardized by an entirely different appreciation of estuarine environments. Until recently, unless useful as deep-water ports, estuaries have been ignored by man as unsightly blemishes on nature's beauty. This indifference has allowed them to flourish in a natural state, whereas forests have been axed and hills leveled. Today, because of their treasured seaside location, estuaries are on the frontline of development. They have qualified for burial by earth fill, better known as "land reclamation."

The overworked dredge has become the estuary's counterpart of the river dam. Dredges busily deepen estuarine channels to accommodate pleasure boats instead of shrimp. The spoil is then used for fill to ac-commodate fish-wharf restaurants, ball parks, housing tracts, and marinas. To speed up the burial cycle cities encourage garbage collectors to dump their harvest on city-owned tidelands. This "sanitary fill" fosters odors far more pungent than those emitted by virgin estuaries —odors that are then cited, paradoxically, as an addi-tional reason to reclaim the estuaries and broaden the property tax base. Fills also shrink the estuary's flushing capacity and concentrate the output of sewer outfalls.

Besides shrinking critical marine habitats, the busy dredges stir up silt movement. If they are not to be buried by this silt, oysters must step up their pumping action to excrete the silt ingested along with the juicy diatoms. This increase may so debilitate the oyster that it will suspend eating operations altogether, risking star-vation. The fact that estuaries are recruited as quarry pits as well as real estate reservoirs intensifies these deadly silt storms. Oyster shell is valuable as road-surfacing material and as aggregate in concrete. It is equally useful in the manufacture of chemicals, limes, and even poultry feed. Oyster-reef deposits, built up over the centuries, provide an abundant source of commercial shell, and suction dredges provide a means of tapping them. The clayish overburden that the dredges remove to reach these dead reefs is discharged into the estuary and, in turn, into the diet of live oyster reefs.

The conflict between oyster-shell mining and oyster-bed cultivation is particularly acute on the Texas Gulf Coast, where the Texas State Conservation Agency is charged with regulating shell-mining operations to avoid live oyster burials. In a recent study Professor Frank Masch of the University of Texas reveals that the state agency has been overrating the ability of currents to disperse mining discharges. Indeed, as noted in Chapter 5, The Haunted Dump, estuarine currents tend to circulate rather than disperse matter. Observes Professor Masch, "Shell dredging is perhaps one of the most critical problems on the Texas Gulf Coast today."

The careless burial of oysters in Texas points up an increasingly dangerous gap in public policy. Although the use of an estuary as a real estate reservoir, a dump, or a sewer discharge or quarry pit is widely accepted practice, its natural values are dimly perceived and little respected. Up to 1961 the valuable estuarine system that fringes the four-thousand-mile South Atlantic and Gulf coastline has rated the full-time attention of but one investigator for the Fish and Wildlife Service. Dr. Wilbert Chapman of Van Camp Sea Food Company, a fishery biologist with three decades of experience, sees an ominous parallel between the lengthy build-up attendant on adequate salmon research facilities and budding estuarine investigations. "We now have a fine research organization but most of the salmon are gone. I think that is what is going to happen in the estuaries to the Gulf of Mexico. About thirty years from now we're going to have a marvelous research organization built up and no shrimp."

The establishment of appropriate institutions to govern proliferating estuary activities proceeds at much the same fatal pace. To maintain a proper balance between estuary development and preservation, a political body with broad powers and a well-informed staff is required, one akin to a soil conservation district or a city planning commission. Yet local and state governments eagerly forfeit their control of estuary tidelands to the polyglot ambitions of marina developers, garbage collectors, and dredge operators. Seductive architectural renderings depict estuaries transformed into luxury residential marinas with a neat shore of concrete bulkheading. Yet the bulkheads are gravestones and the marina a cemetery. The shorebirds are replaced by scavenging gulls, the marine life by rainbow oil spills and the marsh grass by scum algae.

Seton Thompson, who has been watching the gradual burial of St. Petersburg's Boca Ciega Bay from his office window, notes, "These small projects take place in an insidious way—like baldness. A few falling hairs every day go unnoticed until suddenly there is a large bare spot."

There is little incentive to maintaining an estuary in a natural state. "The owner of a salt marsh becomes a public servant," notes the Audubon Society. "The richness of the marsh flows into the sea." Unless the owner also owns a fishing fleet, this sort of flow hardly encourages public beneficence.

The evolving fate of estuaries was clearly summarized in an exchange during a hearing before the Senate Committee on Interior and Insular Affairs. Dr. Stanley Cain of the Department of the Interior was explaining a departmental study on the impact of dredging on Tampa Bay in Florida:

> *Mr. Cain.* Here is a bay in which there must be two dozen species of commercial fish and shellfish that spend part of life. Between fifteen and twenty per cent of the bay has been filled behind bulkheads and, in producing the material for the fill, there has been about an equal percentage of the bay that has been dredged. These studies reveal that after ten years

of dredging the bottom is, in effect, a biological desert. Here is at least a third, perhaps more, of Tampa Bay that has been completely destroyed from the point of view of natural estuary conditions.

Senator Gaylord Nelson (Wisconsin Dem.). So after it is all filled, the ecologists will be able to tell us what happened to it?

Mr. Cain. That brings us to the other point. We have no present means of control over what State and local governments do with respect to endangered habitats.

It is this same situation that imperils a host of small estuaries as well as such large ones as Rhode Island's Narragansett Bay, Delaware Bay, Puget Sound, and that sprawling seafood locker, Chesapeake Bay.

Like the river nurseries, the estuaries are being mauled piecemeal. The Congress is presently considering legislation to save Oyster Bay, a Long Island landmark, from earth-fill burial. (The critical situation of San Francisco Bay is discussed later in the book.) In treating these habitats as incidental casualties of local development rather than as public resources, we cannot help but succeed in destroying the birthright of the salmon and the shad, the shrimp and the oyster, the mullet and the tarpon. Hardly the way to kick off the much-heralded conquest of the ocean's riches. On the other hand, it is a sure way of mocking the government-supported modernization of the American fishing industry. A sonar set may be able to detect bottom shrimp and moving mullet. Only an estuary can produce them.

The ocean may appear to end at the shore, but its vital processes extend into our bays, up our rivers, and even into our mountain streams, where not only salmon but also sandy beaches are born.

TROUBLE IN OUR TIDE POOLS

SHIPOWNERS spend millions of dollars yearly to rid barnacles, mussels and other marine life from the hulls of their ships. While the sea life may be a nuisance

Reprinted from "Westways," 1968, 60(6): 27–28.

to shipowners, ironically, on the rocky shores, where marine life is valuable, another purge is not costing a cent.

That such rockbound marine life, which continually withstands breakers, needs protection may be hard to believe. Yet it does, and the reason lies in its peculiar attractions for that indiscriminate collector—man. No environment—river, valley, desert, open sea or forest— so willingly reveals its life to casual visitors. And what life! The barnacle, the starfish, the flower-like sea anemone appear alien to us, figments of science fiction. They seem eyeless, limbless and senseless, often encased in the anonymity of a shell. Yet these marine creatures have adapted to an environment as rugged as any other on this planet, many being alternatively drenched by the ocean and exposed to sun, wind or rain.

Survival demands special abilities. The acorn barnacle, for instance, secretes its own protective shell and feeds by extending its curled, feathery legs after a wave, rich with minute sea animals, sweeps over it. The starfish can regrow severed limbs and feeds by prying clams open with its tube feet, projecting its stomach inside the disarmed shell and digesting the soft flesh with strong stomach juices. The chiton, a mollusk, uses a tiny, rasping organ to scrape algae off rocks. No environment can boast more astonishing adaptions to survival. And no environment is so conveniently scaled to the world of young children.

As a result, the rocky shore is becoming almost as popular a public attraction as its seductive neighbor, the sandy shore. In this popularity lurk pressures more formidable than battering waves, for while many visitors come only to look, others come armed with buckets, pails, nets and glass jars. Such equipment is employed in the name of collecting, but preservation of marine animals requires specially designed acquaria—something most amateur collectors don't have. Brightly colored plastic pails become, in the words of marine biologist Dr. Gilbert Bane of the University of California at Irvin, "Death Buckets." With hundreds of people descending upon a rocky shore day after summer day, the impact of the bucket brigade becomes apparent. Some collectors pry up rocks to snare shyer species; a few days later, the corpses of sponges, tunicates, worms and corals ring the uprooted habitat.

Another heedlessly destructive collecting method has been used to catch a small octopus (*Octopus bimaculatus*) that nestles in tidal rock hollows. To bag this octopus for the speciality food trade, a harveser squirts liquid nicotine, bleach, bluestone (copper sulfate) or other paralyzing agents into a likely octopus lair. When the dazed octopus deserts its lair, it is easily gaffed. At the same time, the drugs trigger tidal kills.

Dr. Bane once observed a college science class using this same method to collect class specimens. After the class left, Dr. Bane and his students counted the remaining casualties: 1,175 purple sea urchins, 118 common starfish, 27 wooly sculpins, 21 shrimp, 16 octopuses, 11 clingfish, 9 blennies, 8 bat stars, 8 red sea urchins, 4 crabs and 2 opal eyes.

While illegal, this activity is hard to spot, says Robert Kaneen of the California Fish and Game Department. Harvesters can use a small syringe, which is easily hidden in an armpit.

Because of such destructive collecting methods, abalone and octopus are now very rare in the intertidal area. Entire shore areas have been severely depleted. The rocky shores of Laguna Beach and Newport Beach in Southern California have traditionally attracted marine scientists from throughout the country. Yet these areas have been so completely ransacked that a present-day resident, Dr. Bane, often travels to Baja California for specimens once available within walking distance. Mayor Paul Gruber, of Newport Beach, notes that his community's tidal areas are being "looted by numerous individuals, classrooms of school children and other organized groups." In Laguna Beach, City Councilman Glenn Vedder sounded similar warnings.

Senator John A. Murdy (now retired), of Orange County, concerned that valuable rocky tide pools would become ghost tide pools, authored legislation to permit the Department of Fish and Game and the Department of Beach and Parks to recommend ways of protecting the natural values of the coast. These two agencies then recommended the establishment of marine refuges where collecting would be either prohibited or strictly controlled. The Murdy Report cited the existence of pioneer marine refuges: a marine gardens established by Pacific Grove in 1931, a state underwater preserve off Point Lobos State Park and a marine preserve near Scripps Institution of Oceanography in La Jolla.

Based on this report, Laguna Beach, Newport Beach and the Orange County Board of Supervisors proposed three rocky shore areas in need of protection. Each is about a half mile in length and extends offshore to a depth of twenty feet to "permit competition among the marine coastal organisms." As the Murdy Report states, "Nowhere in the land environment is it possible to observe within a small spatial area all the forces and conditions affecting the survival or organisms. To cover a similar environment change on land would require an area that extends from the California coastal seashore eastward to the crest of the Sierra Nevada Mountains." The state approved the preserves.

With the preserves established, marine life harmed by over-collecting should revive rather quickly, according to Caltech marine ecologist Dr. Wheeler North, who wrote to Councilman Vedder: "Given five years of freedom from collection, your marine preserve should be fairly well restored to its natural state." Some species, such as abalone, will require more time to recuperate. At Pacific Grove, a marine refuge patrol of volunteer skin divers helps local and state officials supervise the preserve. The divers receive the same rate of compensation as volunteer firemen.

Preserve status, while restricting collecting activities, will expand other public activities. Dr. North has suggested displays to identify and interpret marine life. Nature tours can be conducted, and marine scientists will have a relatively unspoiled environment available for study. The Murdy Report recommends offering underwater observation facilities, including glass-bottom boats and scuba rentals.

In addition to the support of recreation, conservation and civic action, the preserve idea has attracted the support of marine scientists at the University of California at Irvine and at Los Angeles, at Occidental, at the University of Southern California, at Pomona and at California State College at Long Beach. Supporters know that the rocky shore, rich in its life forms, is an increasingly important scientific resource.

Research in marine biology reaches into many areas: The adhesive compound that barnacles use to fasten themselves to rocks is being investigated as a possible dentrifice to ward off harmful bacteria; and C. P. Li of the National Institute of Health finds "paolin," which can be isolated from abalone juice, will inhibit experimental polio in rats. Scientists also continue studies of the *Gonyaulax cantella* in an effort to predict when and where the "red tide" will occur, and defouling experts, concerned with keeping the hulls of ships free of mussels and barnacles, are studying rocky tidal areas in order to understand the origins of the life systems they have to control.

It would be ironic indeed if such values of the rocky shore were, in time, to be largely confined to the hulls of supertankers. Hopefully, more marine preserves will rescue rocky shores in distress.

9.

The Star-Crossed Whale

A WHALE is a living monument to the grandeur of the ocean. A creature of the land by heritage, the whale inhabits the ocean by choice. On land a whale would be imprisoned by gravity, an easy target for predators one tenth his size. Only the ocean can provide it with the support to buoy its massive size, the food to support its appetite, and the space to accommodate its movements. On land the whale would be as quick as a snail. In the ocean the world's largest mammal can pace an ocean steamer.

Without the whale the ocean would be deprived of its most lordly symbol—and deprived it may well be. The threat to the whale from commercial killing is relatively well known. Yet like the American Indian of the nineteenth century, the whale can face extinction not only by loss of life but by loss by living space. These twin forces of extinction focus with special intensity on a whale species of unique value to man.

Baja California dangles boldly from the southwestern extreme of the continental United States, a geological dagger that plunges into the Pacific and splits the ocean apart from the Gulf of California and northern Mexico. The Sebastian Vizcaino Desert covers the middle of this dagger (160 miles longer than the Italian boot) like rust. Through niches chiseled by combers, the Pacific spills into this desert to form a series of ocean lagoons.

Scientists are not sure of all the reasons that attract the gray, a large whale species forty tons in weight and up to fifty feet in length, to Scammon Lagoon, but they feel that they understand the main ones. To begin with, the lagoon is of a size to accommodate the two thousand or so whales that come annually; a two-mile wide ocean entrance expands into a body of water some thirty-five miles long, up to eleven miles wide, and one hundred twenty feet deep. Instead of a lagoon, this vast body of water resembles a biblical sea that would merge with the sky except for a thin desert horizon. Yet the lagoon, despite its size, generally remains as placid as its counterpart in a municipal park. This can be important to a pregnant whale, who must teach her one-ton baby to breathe and swim immediately. Although these lessons can be learned on the open ocean, swells can complicate matters. The lagoon's high salinity—twice that of the open ocean—provides another benefit, added buoyancy.

Dr. Theodore Walker of Scripps Institution of Oceanography believes that eel-grass beds are another lagoon attraction. Dr. Walker believes that the jaws of the whale scoop up these beds, which are then flushed through the whale's baleen—brushlike filter gums—to expel mud and water and retain shellfish and other eelgrass morsels.

In addition to breeding and feeding attractions, the lagoon offers the gray whale seclusion. Man-made intrusion has caused it to desert its ancient breeding grounds. In Scammon the grays have enjoyed a natural solitude protected by the lagoon's remoteness and inaccessibility to man—at least up to the present.

The whales that enter this desert-flanked lagoon come all the way from their choice feeding grounds in the

Arctic Ocean, a migration of some six thousand miles, or twelve thousand round trip. (A smaller herd summers in the Sea of Okhotsk and winters in the bays of southern Korea.) Despite their massive bulk, restricted vision (whales cannot even see their tails), and impotent sense of smell, the gray whales succeed in making this magnificent migration year after year.

The migrating gray's ability to overcome such natural deficiencies testifies eloquently to his adaptive nature. To make up for deficiencies in sight and smell, the gray utilizes a batlike sense of hearing and organic sonar (echo sounding) that enables him to "see" through sound and navigate the northern Pacific Ocean.

Whale hydrodynamics consists of an economy of motion. The huge bulk is streamlined into an elongated exclamation point with such friction-free features as recessed nipples, ears, and reproductive organs. The streamlined whale has his nostrils on the top of his head. As a result, he never has to thrust his ponderous head out of the water to breathe. Explains Dr. Walker, "The whale comes up from the depths to breathe like a jet coming down to land, everything timed so that only the blowhole breaks through the surface." The whale's flukes, or fanshaped paddle, drive this streamlined body at speeds as high as fifteen knots, a good pace for any large ship.

Equipped with a keen sense of hearing, superb hydrodynamics, and organic food storage, the Arctic-grazing grays head for their desert birthplace in mid-September, followed for a short time by white snowbirds which gorge on their leavings. The grays are a loose, straggling lot in migration, separated by miles of ocean and weeks of time. In the lead are the pregnant whales, which set a pace of about one hundred miles a day. This informal procession passes through the Chukchi and Bering seas before the cold waters stiffen to ice, loops around the Aleutian Islands, and trails along the coast of British Columbia. Occasionally some members of the procession pause to rub their barnacle-encrusted torsos against the anchor chains of a Canadian lightship.

By November the procession passes within sight of Cape Flattery, a lonely headland in Washington. Countless blows, or "plumes," form rainbow prisms in the light of the ocean sun. Soon yachtsmen out of San Francisco can watch certain whales exchange taps with their front stabilizer flippers. Because these exchanges occur between males and eligible females, they are regarded as love taps. They resound for miles.

Occasionally, a group of grays will hastily meld into a giant, revolving pinwheel with their limber tails as spokes. This formation wards off the wolflike packs of toothed killer whales. (The U. S. Navy once depthbombed killer whales who were swallowing Iceland's fishing economy.) That is another of Scammon Lagoon's attractions: an absence of the swift killer whales.

By late December this rainbow-plumed procession tightens up and passes in review off Point Loma, a San Diego headland. About three hundred miles south of Point Loma and three weeks later the lead pregnant whales come within echo sounding of submerged sandbars. "No definite directions can be given for crossing the bar at Scammon, which is constantly changing," notes the U. S. Navy Hydrographic Office. Like Phantom beaches, these submerged bars trip up the offshore swells and create a surf in the middle of the rolling blue sea. They guard the entrance to the placid lagoons of Baja California and tell the gray whales that they have reached their destination. The grays, with a draft of six to eight feet, thread their way through the submerged obstacle course.

The grays have three major breeding areas: San Ignacio Lagoon, the lagoon channels in Magdalena Bay, and Scammon Lagoon. Scammon attracts the largest number, approximately two thousand. During January and February they are so profuse that their constant blows endow the lagoon with a built-in sprinkler system. If you venture into this whale lagoon in a boat, you will find that the whales become navigational hazards. In the near distance a glistening rubbery hull rends the calm waters, spouts a minor geyser of condensed breath, and slips silently back beneath the blue cover of the lagoon. Without warning, but fifteen yards away, a sonorous exhalation sounds, like the whoosh of a steam press, and a blowhole, spewing like a volcanic island, emerges. A cloud of vapor vanishes, exposing the two dark pits that mark the nostrils, and a long grayish-black hull crusted with knobby barnacles trails the submerging blowhole. You watch, rooted in amazement, as the mere backbone of a whale instantly cuts everything in the world down to size. Then, to the rear, a smaller blowhole emerges, spouts, and sounds. A newborn calf is following the lead of its mother.

Sometimes a whale's mighty forward torso will shoot out of the water like a metal pile and then topple in an explosion of foam. This maneuver is called "breaching." Another whale will emerge from the lagoon depths in what is called a "spy hop" as casually as a cobra from a basket. His lower jaw unhinges like a drawbridge and the desert sky becomes pinioned in his open mouth. The jaws close slowly on the sky and the head sinks back beneath the water.

The terms that designate these impressive maneuvers are merely descriptive. Scientists differ on what, if anything, is being accomplished. Dr. Walker connects spy hopping with feeding. "It is my theory," says the Scripps scientist, "that the whale assumes this vertical position—sometimes with its flukes (tails) actually on the bottom to help support it—because this posture brings the heavier seafood to the bottom of its throat where it is easier to swallow. The throat muscles can actually be seen swallowing." Some scientists speculate that spy hops are a form of male chauvinism, for they occur repeatedly in one narrow neck of the lagoon. This particular body of water, referred to by scientists as Fornication Hole, is where whales mate. Here whale taps thunder and whale heads collide affectionately. During this foreplay the male's eight-foot penis emerges from its recessed pocket. The courting pair then merge close to the surface and begin revolving like a cumbersome lathe. Whales are polygamous and a high level of activity is maintained in the mating area.

When an impregnated female returns to Scammon the following year, she passes through Fornication Hole with a one-ton baby in her womb. She cruises into more spacious waters called the Nursery. Gulls, which congregate to feast on the afterbirth, indicate to human observers when the underwater birth has occurred. In a frenzied cloud of white feathers, a new mother will lift her head clear of the water. On top is the baby, some fifteen feet long. The mother's head submerges and re-emerges with the baby whale perched in the same place. The mother is teaching her newborn to breathe. Otherwise, two round-trip migrations, twenty-four thousand miles in all, will go for naught. After a while the calf will nestle close to its mother's underside near the surface. The recessed nipples form an airtight connection with the calf's mouth which shuts out the salt water. To expedite the feeding the calf does not suck. The mother squirts a gallon or two of milk down the calf's throat.

After six weeks in the Nursery the mother leaves Scammon, trailed by her calf who will be fully weaned in the microshrimp pastures of the Arctic Ocean. It will be the first of many migrations for this baby whale. How many is not known because scientists do not know how long whales live.

The gray's affinity for coastal waters, in particular a desert-flanked lagoon, is unique in whaledom. Other large whale species steer clear of coastal waters; on leaving the freezing polar seas in the fall, they seek out island sanctuaries—the Azores, Malagasy, Melanesia, New Zealand—to winter in uninhabited inlets and atoll lagoons. Precisely because of its affinity for coastal waters, the gray becomes a bellwether of the whale's ability—or lack of ability—to survive the forces of man.

In the nineteenth century Yankee whalers ventured into the open seas to track down the big blubber whales, following creatures faster and larger than their own ships through icy gales, dead calms, and uncharted waters. In January of 1846 a New England whaling ship en route to the polar grounds of the prized bow-head whale came to anchor in Magdalena Bay. The astonished crew saw countless whale spouts pricking through the calm blue surface of the bay lagoons. A whale-killing spree promptly ensued. What was patron-izingly dubbed the "mudhole season" came into being. This patronization obscured a salient trait of lagoon whaling. On the open seas, a whale—once he was har-pooned—tended to run and sound in the hope of shaking loose the whale boat that clung fast to the end of the harpoon line. The shallow, confined nature of the la-goon thwarted this running tactic and forced the gray whale to meet his tormentors head on. Because the grays were more agile than the whaling boats, the pursuers suddenly found themselves the object of pur-suit. Sometimes the harpooned gray would corner his tormentors and ram their wooden craft. Sometimes his mightly flukes would clear the water and crash down on the luckless whaling crew in a tactic called "lobtail-ing," and sometimes the line on a boat made "fast" to a whale would suddenly go slack. The perplexed crew would look over the side of the boat to sight the whale, but the waters would be murky with mud and sand churned up by their quarry. Then, in a frightful flash, the crew would be lifted clear of the lagoon and sent flying through the air. The whale, playing possum, sim-ply waited for the lagoon current to bring the whale boat overhead . . . and into position for a reverse lob-tail. "I shipped to go a-whaling," complained one sur-viving lobtail victim to his captain. "I'd no idea of bein' required to go into a duck pond to whale after spotted hyenas." The gray's deadly cunning resulted in a bad press and temporarily discouraged exploitation of the whale ponds, but commercial pressure on whalers to confront the "devil fish" increased.

In 1857 the brig *Boston* entered a previously ignored

lagoon. On the debut of whaling in its waters, a jubilant captain, Charles Melville Scammon, could report, "Two large cows were captured without difficulty, which gave all hands confidence in our ultimate success." This confidence crumbled the next day. Before a whale could even be struck (harpooned), two of the *Boston's* three whaling boats were staved in by a succession of flashing flukes. Scammon found himself in command of "a crowded and contracted hospital. Our situation was both singular and trying. The vessel lay in perfect security in smooth water; and the objects of pursuit, which had been so anxiously sought, were now in countless numbers about us."

One morning a boat was lowered from the "contracted and crowded hospital." The crew carefully hugged the shallow lagoon shoreline, out of reach of the whales, and finally anchored inshore where the lagoon narrowed into Fornication Hole. When a whale emerged to spout, a man in the boat shouldered a new form of technology. The bomb-lance gun fired a bomb lance designed to pierce the whale's blubber and timed to detonate inside the whale's lungs. It had one drawback—a short range. When the whale emerged again, the man aimed and fired. When the color of the whale's spout turned crimson, the man knew he had successfully pressed the gun's range.

On the open seas such marksmanship would have been futile. A "bombed" whale would sink or, once it floated to the surface, be out of sight. Scammon hoped that the lagoon, by its largely enclosed nature, would make the bombed whale fast. The following day, the whale was floating near the head of the lagoon, buoyed up by gases decomposing in its blubbery hull. Scammon was no longer in the business of pursuing whales. He was ambushing them.

In one season Scammon had not only discovered a prime breeding ground of the gray whale but had devised a means of making the defiant grays as defenseless as steers in a stockyard. Bustling boat crews knitted shut the giant lips of dead whales and towed the bloated

A school of perch cruises through the kelp fronds of California's verdant sea forests.—*Charles Turner, California Department of Fish and Game.*

A once-verdant sea forest is being stripped bare by hundreds of tiny, spiky urchins that cluster around the kelp holdfast. Scientists now believe that coastal sewage outfalls may corrupt marine ecology and transform the urchins into voracious kelp predators.—*California Institute of Technology.*

In the immediate foreground rests a dredge. In the background stands a creature of the dredge, an artificial oil-well island. Like the sewage outfall, the indiscriminate use of dredges may jeopardize the ocean's living resources.

An oil slick approaching a southern California beach will shut down swimming, sun bathing, boating, and fishing for a few days. This slick was variously blamed on ships' bilges, an offshore oil-well leak, and an earthquake-nudged submarine seep. As in too many other cases of ocean pollution, its actual cause remains a mystery.—*United States Coast Guard.*

Man has been dumping junk into the ocean for centuries, but only lately has he been doing it in a constructive manner. This old car forms an artificial fish habitat. The fish in the foreground seem to approve.— *Charles Turner, California Department of Fish and Game.*

On the left, a Pacific Ocean sunset; on the right, a California sewage outfall. The popularity of this simple form of disposal now threatens the living resources of the coastal ocean.

This modest estuary is a nursery for the sea, nurturing millions of fish, shellfish, and waterfowl. Like too many other life-giving estuaries, its existence is threatened by sewage outfalls, dredging projects, land reclamation, and other aspects of coastal development.

A gray whale emerges from Mexico's Scammon Lagoon in a spy hop.

Scammon Lagoon also nurtures solar salt mountains like this one. Unless properly regulated, solar salt activities threaten to evict the gray whales.

Chicago has kept faith with Daniel Hudson Burnham's belief that an urban waterfront need not be an industrial gutter.—*Chicago Department of Planning and Development.*

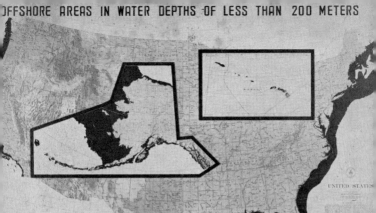

This chart depicts the seabed of America's continental shelf. Rich in potential resources, some 850,000 square miles in extent, varying in width from less than 5 miles off California to upwards of 250 miles off New England and Alaska, this seabed poses critical problems of development and management.—*United States Coast and Geodetic Survey.*

These sleek tuna await processing into tuna salad sandwiches. This valuable food source sparks one of the world's fiercest fishery competitions.

America's most advanced fisherman, the tuna fisherman, mends a gigantic purse seine. The ocean-wide success of this net helps to inspire Latin American countries to indulge in galloping sea sovereignty and tuna-boat seizures.

California Conservation Camp Inmates supervised by the California Division of Forestry are shown spreading straw to absorb oil on Leadbetter Beach in Santa Barbara. The Santa Barbara Yacht Club is in the background, center.

The promise and the problem of ocean conquest exemplified. Used militarily, submarines can initiate a clandestine undersea arms race. Used peacefully, submarines can develop and colonize the undersea. Used carelessly, they can exhaust the marine environment.— *Northrup Corporation.*

corpses to the trying pots. Stinking smoke from the trying pots spiraled into the desert sky accompanied by the babble of Portuguese, Kanaka, and Yankee tongues.

A sudden influx of whalers fostered further refinements on the lagoon slaughter. A whale boat would chase a stray calf into the lagoon shallows. Soon the anxious mother would appear to retrieve her young, only to strand in the shallows. Once the mother was caught fast by the low tide and her own frantic exhaustion, the whaling boat would reappear for the kill.

Lagoon whaling was soon practiced just as intensively in other lagoons, small and large, along the Baja coastline. While this maritime carnival reveled in the gray's breeding grounds, eleven whaling stations along the California coastline bushwhacked grays en route to the lagoons. This commercial aggression could have but one end. By 1861, four years after Scammon sailed into his lagoon, gray whaling was no longer economical. Too few grays were left. Since the initiation of lagoon whaling an estimated ten thousand eight hundred whales had gone into the trying pots. This mortality did not include the calves who endlessly circled the ships where they had last seen their mothers until starvation set in. The whalers departed from the desert lagoons to find new grounds and to apply new techniques. From a prewhaling population of some thirty thousand, the grays descended to "no more than a few dozen," according to one San Diego naturalist who missed their lordly procession off Point Loma in the 1930's. Ironically, the grays' vulnerability to whaling suddenly contributed to their survival.

In 1938 the International Convention for the Regulation of Whaling instituted a voluntary method of conservation quotas on whale kills. The convention also accorded the gray a special status in recognition of its plundered condition. "It is forbidden to take or kill gray whales except when the meat and products of such whales are to be used exclusively for local consumption by the aborigines."

With Scammon Lagoon off limits to whaling captains,

the grays have brought their population level up to an estimated six thousand, but the beneficent clause of the International Convention protects them only from commercial exploitation. It does not protect their vital living space, and thus they once again face the threat of ultimate extinction.

The Vizcaino Desert helps to make Baja California one of Mexico's least populated regions, but it does manage to host one small community, a prosperous one at that. Guerrero Negro is surrounded by the source of its prosperity, giant solar salt ponds that stretch out of sight like snow-covered prairies. The saline-rich waters of Scammon Lagoon which buoy up baby whales are pumped into these ponds at the rate of 387 million gallons daily. To up annual salt production from one million to three million tons, Exportadora de Sal, owner of the 300,000-acre salt concession, is in the process of dredging part of the lagoon as a loading dock and a salt barge channel. Barges will transship the salt harvest to 100,000-ton tankers which can not worm their way through submerged sand bars.

Exportadora, which spent sixteen million dollars to construct the saltworks complex, will spend an additional twenty million to realize expansion plans. The prime obstacle to such ambitious plans ordinarily would be financing, but not in Exportadora's case. Exportadora is an affiliate of National Bulk Carriers, Inc., of the United States, which in turn is controlled by D. K. Ludwig of New York. Besides owning outright the world's pioneer fleet of supertankers, Mr. Ludwig dredges the Orinoco River in Venezuela to accommodate his iron-ore tankers. (Recently he wanted to dredge a twelve-mile channel through the Everglades country of Dade County, Florida. The dredged-up portion of Everglades, some forty-five million cubic yards in all, would provide earth fill for the site of a petrochemical-harbor complex, but Mr. Ludwig could not obtain a zoning variance for such nature moving. Wildlife groups and Miami tourist interests, rallied by resident-author Philip Wylie, successfully protested that the price of the channel project would be the scenic beauty and abundant life of the Everglades.)

Although the fourteen hundred residents of Guerrero Negro, whose homes, shops, and gypsum roads are owned by Exportadora, are understandably happy over the expansion plans, scientists who faithfully trek to Scammon Lagoon each January to document the gray's return from the "extinct and vanishing category" are much less so. In 1960, before Exportadora began turning towards Scammon, Dr. Raymond Gilmore, conductor of a gray-whale census for the U. S. Fish and Wildlife Service, wrote, "The area available for calving and mating may be the most critical factor in determining eventual size of population. Reduction of this area by natural events or by man may have a pronounced effect in lowering the population ceiling." Today Dr. Gilmore sees in the plans of Exportadora the seeds of just such a "pronounced effect."

Such scientific premonition is based on the nature of the whale and a reading of history. The whale's craving for seclusion, as offered by Scammon Lagoon, is no mere whim. In "seeing" through sound, whales can be temporarily blinded by distracting noises, such as the hum of a ship's screws, the moan of harbor dredges, or the clatter of loading docks. The century-old desertion by the grays of San Diego Bay as a winter home coincided with harbor development. A hundred years later, Dr. Gilmore sees the whale's low tolerance to noise re-enacted in Magdalena Bay, where increasing fishing-boat traffic caused the "gray whales to consort in numbers only in the inaccessible tributaries." (Magdalena Bay is now being transformed into a five million dollar deep-water port and seaside playground.)

Oily barge emissions raise another discouraging possibility: eventual pollution of the eel-grass beds.

Although initial barging activity at Scammon will occur in a lagoon arm not regularly frequented by the whales—a company decision based on engineering considerations, not conservation—there is no specified end to lagoon "development." (The narrow channel through the shifting sand bars will foster whale-barge encounters outside the lagoon.) With whale requirements at the mercy of salt requirements, an eviction of whales from Scammon Lagoon becomes possible, either gradually or quite suddenly. Faced with a continuing takeover of its winter grounds in Baja California, the gray will have to find new coastal breeding and feeding grounds, compete with other whale species for offshore grounds, or subsist on the open ocean. The uncertainty of such adaption intensifies scientific concern.

Such a prospect has a particularly galling significance to scientists. Just like commercial whalers, highbrow whalers must generally take to the open seas to track down the object of their professional curiosity. But observing a whale from a ship—if one is sighted—is like observing an iceberg; most of what matters is not visible. As a result, even though factory ships know how to slaughter whales on an assembly-line basis, scientists know distressingly little about a creature that pumps blood through hundreds of feet of arteries at one pulse, maintains a body temperature of ninety-six degrees in near freezing waters, manufactures a mother's milk twice as rich as that of human mothers, and possesses a sponge-like bone structure that can redeem multifractures.

The almost unbelievable opportunity that Scammon Lagoon provides—a pondlike atmosphere in which to observe the world's largest mammal intimately—was first recognized by Captain Scammon, incredibly enough. While ordering harpooners to bomb whales, the self-educated Scammon was also measuring the girth of the victims, inspecting the contents of their stomachs, and executing precise drawings of their magnificent torsos. Like another whaling contemporary, Herman Melville, Scammon sensed that there was more to whales than oil to light cities and bone to corset can-can lines. In 1874 he made what the magazine *Science* soon declared was "the most important contribution to the life history of marine mammals ever published": *The Marine Mammals of the North-western Coast of North America.*

With the gray whale in the almost extinct category around the turn of the century, Scammon Lagoon slipped from scientific notice. In 1926 a famous Hollywood actor was cruising through the lagoons of Baja California in his yacht *The Gypsy*. John Barrymore was entranced by two gray whales in "amorous dalliance . . . if anything so enviably and titanically active comes under the heading of dalliance." He whipped out his camera. "We eavesdropped, and I trust, for the stimulus of one's old age, recorded the largest mammals in flagrante delicto! A memorable day!" Barrymore, who harpooned a gassy rubber facsimile of a whale in the movie "The Sea Beast," then tried to accomplish the real thing on a gray, but failed, according to his biographer Gene Fowler.

Errol Flynn, a good friend of Barrymore, was thrilled by these encounters. Shortly after World War II the swashbuckling actor, son of an Australian biologist, personally chauffeured a Scripps scientist to Scammon in his somewhat infamous yacht. Dr. Carl Hubbs, an ardent reader of Captain Scammon's lifework, confirmed that the gray whales existed in goodly numbers in the lagoon. This confirmation has since sparked eager scientific pilgrimages.

These pilgrimages have often been confined to testing, and sometimes discarding, techniques designed to overcome the whale's size and surprising sensitivity. Dr. Paul Dudley White, heart specialist to Presidents, thought it would be instructive to record the heartbeat of a whale. He set off for Scammon Lagoon with an electronic harpoon, a harpoon crew, and a swift outboard. Unfortunately, Dr. White's crew drifted between a mother whale and her calf, and the mother nearly staved in their boat with a flick of her flukes. Dr. White then resorted to a hovering helicopter, but the grays proved too agile for aerial harpooning.

Scammon Lagoon also attracts acoustical physicists,

armed with buoy hydrophones, who seek to record and identify whale sounds. It seems that the U. S. Navy cannot always tell a whale sound from a submarine sound, and this is not a healthy situation, either for the Navy or the whale. Lagoon whales, whether or not they know they are being bugged, tend to remain silent in the vicinity of buoy hydrophones. Two physicists were reduced to writing a scientific paper entitled "The Silent Whale." "Submarines go silent when they are being spied on," suggests Dr. Walker, "why not whales?"

In his study of whale behavior Dr. Walker generally scorns exaggerated technology. On occasion he has used a rowboat topped with a plywood forecastle that looks as if it were recruited from the rental stock of a park pond. With the motion of the lagoon tidal current, Dr. Walker likes to creep up on a forty-five-foot whale until its occasional blow virtually clouds in *Walker's Ark*. "Creeping a whale" gives Dr. Walker intimate glimpses of bull whales napping and cow whales feeding, but unnerves guest observers, including myself, who have seen a whale pass beneath the *Ark* like a silent freight train.

As oceanographers like Dr. Walker comprehend the organic system that sustains the world's largest mammal, other oceanographers speculate on how this knowledge might be utilized. In "Ocean Engineering," a voluminous study by North American Aviation, the high cost of obtaining and equipping vessels specific to collect oceanographic data is discussed. The placing of sensors for temperature, salinity, and other factors on wide-ranging marine animals is posed as a possible solution. The study notes, "As an example, the California gray whale ranges from Lower California, up the Pacific Coast to Alaskan waters. . . . At the same time, it moves from the surface to great depths; thus, an animal is available to randomly probe a large volume of the Pacific waters. It also surfaces several times an hour and could, therefore, telemeter recorded information at that time. If many ships were provided with simple recording and automatic direction finding equipment, the data transmitted could be reduced to a practical form on an almost continuous basis." This proposed solution ends with a note of caution. "The hazards of working with this animal are not to be underestimated, however."

As a scientific whale observatory Scammon Lagoon could in time become the place in which the whales could reveal their natural secrets to man. As a general whale observatory it could become the place in which the gray whale could display its grandeur to the world. Already the gray is a major tourist attraction in southern California, an area in which the competition is fairly hectic. Each December the National Park Service operates the world's pioneer whale observatory on strategic Point Loma. In addition, three San Diego sport-fishing firms operate "whale-hunt" boats, which put passengers "practically out on the backs of whales," according to Dr. Walker. These passengers pay just to see the backs and blows of whales. Yet three hundred miles to the south they could watch whales breaching, spy hopping, sleeping, nursing, and mating, just from the shoreline.

As roads and modest tourist accommodations penetrate Baja California's scenic remoteness Scammon Lagoon could achieve its potential as a world-famous whale observatory—*if* rigorously supervised. Water ski rentals, whale-hunt boats, and sewage outfalls could chase away the grays even more quickly than plodding salt barges. Governed properly, Scammon Lagoon might well function as both a salt-barge channel and an observatory. Although scientists believe that whales have a low tolerance for man-made activity, they do not yet know the threshold levels of this tolerance. If such levels could be established by a program of yearly monitoring at Scammon, regulations on barging activity might be formulated. That the whales occupy Scammon but two months of the year could facilitate acceptance of these regulations.

Mexico possesses the authority to implement such a program. Yet conservation in a developed nation is difficult enough to achieve; in a developing nation it is an even more trying task. Just as it was in San Diego Harbor a century ago, the plight of the gray whales can be totally obscured by immediate considerations of economic development, for when the government of Mexico thinks of Scammon Lagoon it must consider Exportadora de Sal as well as whales. For a country striving to improve the lot of its people, Exportadora has colonized a desert area, installed an ocean harbor, created an important export commodity, made Mexico the third leading salt producer among developing nations, and now promises to equal that achievement among the developed nations as well. Unlike Dade County, Florida, Mexico is not particularly inclined to interfere with the visions of Mr. Ludwig.

Although signatory to the International Convention that protects the grays, Mexico has considered opening up whaling on them. In 1965 Mexico asked for and received bids for a whaling station that would convert lagoon whales into oil and whale steaks. Although inopportune from the viewpoint of the convention or conservation, such a station might provide a quick financial killing. The harpoon cannon and the factory ship have made the mighty blue whale as vulnerable to purges as the gray, so vulnerable that whaling is at its lowest ebb. Two firms from Japan, a large whaling nation (also signatory to the whaling convention), are among the eager bidders, even though the gray-whale stocks cannot ensure a long commercial life for the station. The plans have not yet come to fruition. If they do, the whalers of the United States, Canada, and Russia cannot be expected to sit idly by as the grays migrate down to a Mexican whaling station.

One agency in the Mexican government now appears to dissent from the proposal. In the fall of 1966 Dr. Enrique Beltran, director of the Mexican Institute of Renewable Natural Resources, forwarded to me a letter he received from Jorge Echaniz, Mexico's General Director of Fishing. Mr. Echaniz said his department was drawing up a "recommendation for the protection of this species (the gray whale) which will define our opinions on this matter, essentially pointing up the necessity of building a sanctuary in Laguna Ojo de Liebre (Scammon Lagoon)." Mr. Echaniz expressed concern that Exportadora boats had already caused whales to move away from Guerrero Negro Lagoon. He also indicated concern over gray whaling. "No path should be left open for its possible exploitation, since it has taken thirty years for the species' recuperation, and it could be easily lost by a brief lapse into irrational capture."

If such views are politely filed away, Mexico's economic ambition will join all the other forces that bear down on the gray whales of Scammon Lagoon with the intensity of a conspiracy—the world-wide industrial appetite for salt, the solar-salt qualities of the Vizcaino Desert, the business acumen of D. K. Ludwig, the evolution of supertankers, the muscular technology of deepwater dredging, and the weakness of whaling conservation. The main ally of the whales, inaccessibility, crumbles before these forces. Only man himself can provide the protection that this ally once offered. Dr. Gilmore, who has watched the grays recover from one disaster, concludes, "The gray whale is a relict species in a shrinking environment."

Because other large whales steer clear of coastal waters is no guarantee that man's industrious nature will bypass their grounds. Smaller whale species who do favor coastal haunts have already felt the brunt of this shrinking environment. For three hundred fifty dollars a tourist can harpoon a white beluga whale in Canada's Hudson Bay from a canoe outfitted with an outboard engine. Other members of the marine mammal family are also undergoing the tribulations of civilization. The U. S. Navy utilizes San Miguel Island as a "danger zone," that is, a punching bag for missile salvos. This small isolated island off southern California happens to be one of the last major American haunts of the sea elephant, a two-ton edition of a seal. Like the gray whale, the sea elephant was once hunted to near extinction. Like the gray whale, the sea elephant recovered from the "vanishing" category through prohibitions on commercial killing. Like the gray whale, the sea elephant now faces eviction from a vital breeding ground. (The Union Oil blowout in the Santa Barbara Channel doused part of the island rookey grounds; investigators found 45 oil-smeared seals on the verge of death.)

The threat of such evictions will occur with increasing frequency until international forms of protection effectively preserve the living space as well as the life stocks of marine mammals. Such agreements have been evolved to protect migratory waterfowl. Because of the whale's oceanwide migration habits, its protection will require the cooperation of nations at all levels of economic development and conservation management. This is a large order, but without such organized foresight whales will follow the buffalo, the mountain gorilla, and the bald eagle to extinction. It seems inconceivable, but so is the very existence of a whale—even when you see one emerge from the quiet waters of Scammon Lagoon in a gallant spy hop.

10.

In Search of Mermaids

AN ocean far different from Byron's impenetrable redoubt confronts us today. Heat, noise, sewage, DDT, breakwaters, harpoon guns, and dams can disrupt its processes and, in turn, our own marine ambitions. This careless corruption springs from an appreciation out of balance. Although we value the ocean as a resource, we appreciate it very little as an environment. The potential wealth of the ocean is zealously surveyed, measured, and ballyhooed; its tolerances are much less so.

Like a steer branded, the land bears the mark of this imbalance. In the nineteenth century our machines really began to work the earth. The pistons quickened in this century. These machines now provide us paradoxically with great natural wealth and an environment badly in need of repair, right down to the very air we breathe. Exploitation of the land easily becomes the means of exhausting it. Hills defrocked of their forests slowly melt under summer rains. Television commercials exalt supercleansing detergents; Lake Erie stands quarantined by detergent (and other) discharges. A better appreciation of our environment could have forestalled its fouling and the monumental cleansing job now in uncertain progress.

The situation in the ocean becomes distressingly familiar. Its exploiters are working at cross purposes. While fishermen eagerly invest in sonar sets and other exotic fish detectors, their quarry is being walled off from an integral part of its environment by dams and earth fills. States acquire expensive public beaches while coastal cities, with the occasional counsel of the Corps of Engineers, erect breakwaters that uproot the expensive acquisitions. At the same time, as corporations build costly mining dredges, Naval gunnery practice entombs rich marine mineral deposits. Without even living inside the ocean, we can degrade it as easily as we degrade the land. It is almost as if desecration has been computerized and placed under remote control.

The ocean obviously requires respect for its limitations as well as its strength. Arrogance toward the ocean's capacity to absorb wastes can be just as deadly as arrogance toward its ability to roll a Navy destroyer. Without such respect, there will be a duplication of the land's fate. Cries of "Desecration" and "Don't disturb nature!" will be countered by "You can't stop progress!" There will be quests for the last gray whale and there will be heated conservation disputes, but this time, nations as well as groups of private citizens will be involved.

To cultivate a broad appreciation of the ocean is a formidable task. It is easy to see when a forest is being mistreated. There is a profusion of stumps. Raindrops coalesce into liquid knives that gully the forest floor. Fewer leaves and twigs rustle underfoot. Life is stilled. The forest dies visibly.

The ocean may be deep blue and the waves may be rising as though the ocean were standing on end. Yet the sardine schools may be thinned, the kelp forests receding, and the waters laced with toxic substances. The ocean dies invisibly. Neither bold tree stumps nor harsh gullies alert us to the danger.

The ocean cannot only veil its true condition but its inner workings as well. Dip a glass into the ocean and out comes water. It is hard to discern the intricate inter-action of the saline content, the nutrient levels, the currents, and the tides. Sophisticated instruments may read these signs, yet we can still be blind to their larger significance. A breakwater may fit in with the ocean's regime in one area; in another it may be as out of place as a U-turn on a Los Angeles freeway.

Mariners once told of bare-breasted young ladies, called mermaids, who threaded ships through the jaws of rocks and the eyes of hurricanes. Their forms decorated the bows of ships to charm tall waves and seduce black skies. To guide us through the maze of our marine ambitions and powers we need mermaids just as versatile, knowledgeable, and assured.

The search for a means to develop a more comprehensive grasp of the ocean environment naturally leads to institutions of higher learning. The United States has some fine ocean research organizations—Woods Hole in Massachusetts and Scripps at the University of California at San Diego are perhaps the best known; but these institutions depend largely on support from the Navy, the dominant spender in ocean research. Although it displays a great interest in general ocean research, the Navy must inevitably allocate most of its funds to naval problems. Nor can the Navy concern itself with apportioning funds to ensure that all coastal states receive an equal opportunity to study their environments.

In the last century Senator Justin Smith Morrill of Vermont was concerned with the lack of broad under-standing of another enormous resource, the land. Land tillage was becoming an increasingly important part of the American economy, yet eroded farmland and depleted or wasted resources indicated the need for greater agricultural knowledge. Higher education, as it was then structured, did not seem too ready to help. Organized on the European classical tradition, the universities concentrated on theology, mathematics, classical languages, and philosophy. The Senator (son of a Vermont smithy) found these universities fit for "teaching only those destined to pursue the so-called learned professions."

The Senator decided to propose a college system that would make agriculture as worthy of research training, and contemplation as the dead languages. The United States had many public lands. The states could be given these properties to sell to help finance colleges devoted to the study of the land, particularly as an agricultural resource. In 1858 President Buchanan vetoed Senator Morrill's Land Grant Act, but Jonathan Baldwin Turner, a professor from downstate Illinois, secured a pledge of support from Buchanan's successor. At the height of the Civil War President Lincoln signed Senator Morrill's concept into law.

The knowledge generated by land-grant colleges has made the American soil the richest agricultural resource in the world. Never have 190 million people been so free from hunger. An American farmer today produces enough to sustain himself and thirty-eight other people. The efficient practices initiated by agricultural experiment stations also provide a critical release of agricultural manpower to meet growing industrial needs. Although supporting only seven per cent of the nation's employment, agriculture accounts for more than a fourth of the nation's total export earnings. (In 1965 fishery imports equaled more than one third of our deficit balance of payments.) Land-grant college graduates have contributed enormously to world-wide agricultural practices, and today are helping young nations to realize the yield of the earth. It is unfortunate that the eroded farmland that inspired Senator Morrill's idea could not have been set aside as an example. Its gullies would underscore the disaster to which an insufficiently broad appreciation of nature can ultimately lead.

Dr. Athelstan Spilhaus directs the Institute of Technology at the University of Minnesota. Born in Cape Town, South Africa, he came to the United States in 1931. At Woods Hole he pioneered in developing instruments such as the bathythermograph to read the ocean's condition. Long before it became a fashionable scientific and political stance Dr. Spilhaus was advocating increased national efforts in the ocean. His interest led him to consider the success of Senator Morrill's concept. In 1963 at a meeting of the American Fisheries Society he proposed a sea-grant college system. In 1965 a national conference on the Concept of a Sea-Grant University convened at the University of Rhode Island. That same year Senator Claiborne Pell, the junior senator from Rhode Island, introduced a sea-grant college bill. In 1966 President Johnson signed just such a measure into law. The nation had dedicated to the oceans something to which our high-powered space program cannot even lay claim —a national college system. Here lies what may be the major opportunity to groom new mermaids who will ultimately render the oceans transparent. The bill aims at setting up sea-grant branches within existing university systems.

An issue critical to the success of the concept will be distribution of funds. States that can claim Scripps, Woods Hole, or other institutions nurtured by Navy funds are ideally prepared to claim many of the sea grants. Other states, particularly along the valuable Gulf and Atlantic estuarine coasts and the Great Lakes, lack such a headstart. "Your Sea-Grant University idea is one of the most important ones that has been advanced in eradicating the lopsided regional studies of our ocean shores, if it is properly written and properly applied," Dr. Gordon Gunter, director of Gulf Coast Research Laboratory, observed to Senator Pell during hearings on the bill. Such sentiments should not be dismissed as mere pork barreling. The Sea-Grant bill should serve to remedy an imbalance of capabilities.

Coastal states can now set aside aquaculture and marine preserves to complement sea-grant campuses. Preservation of tidepools becomes especially critical. (Copper sulfate crystals have been dropped into tidepools in southern California to drug and snare octopi for the fish market.) Lakes would benefit greatly from the same foresight. No one really knew seventy-five years ago that the new Scripps Institution of Oceanography stood beside two unique marine phenomena, La Jolla and Scripps submarine canyons. Students explore and experiment in these canyons daily, as well as in a marshland preserve and a one-square-mile ocean preserve shared with the Naval Electronics Laboratory off San Diego. A most impressive campus. To get around on its campus, as well as on the world oceans, Scripps operates a fleet of vessels from its own harbor. A prospective power plant and sewage outfall threatens to jeopardize a clean ocean area off Scripps and the state is being asked to set aside an underwater preserve seventeen miles long and more than half a mile wide.

The curriculum at a sea-grant college may pose a problem. Robert Abel, administrator of the national sea grant program, notes:

> Consider, if you will, what we plan to do to this student. We're going to immerse him in engineering. We will flavor this immersion with some law and home economics; we will push him part way through a sanitation laboratory. . . . He's going to spend considerable time at sea if he's a worthwhile student, and this will, of course, prolong his stay at school, four, five, six, perhaps seven years. This is the history of oceanography, as you well know. Now, what's he doing all this time? He's certainly prevented from holding down a conventional job ashore. In his shore hours he cannot normally be an assistant because, as you know, there are almost no undergraduate departments in oceanography where he can help students, and so he must have unique sources of income available to him. Now, all this time that he has prolonged his education he has been raising a family, and this simply adds to his financial discomfort. That is why, you see, this concept of sea-grant support is particularly precious to me. I believe there is going to be a lot of work in it from the point of view of the student.

The ocean will demand much of those who propose to comprehend it. On the other hand, I recall waking aboard a Scripps vessel in the silence of Scammon Lagoon, seeing a whale breach against the dawn horizon, and watching Dr. Walker sip morning coffee while taking notes on marine marvels. The ocean does require the dedication of its students, but in return it is prepared to charm, entertain, and fascinate.

Much of the applied spirit of the land-grant colleges

spills over into the sea-grant concept. Dr. Spilhaus observes:

> The sea-grant college, to do its job, will also need its county agents in hip boots—an Aquacultural Extension Service that takes the findings of the college or university onto the trawlers, drilling rigs, merchant ships, and down to the sub-motels. . . . Even if we had abundant protein from the sea today, a selling job would need to be done to remove taste prejudices and taboos.

At the same time, Dr. Spilhaus recognizes the ocean scholar's need for a broad intellectual spirit.

> Just as the scholars in the land-grant college developed a passion for the land and led not only in ways to benefit by it, but also in ways to preserve it—we must seek through a welding together of science, art, literature, engineering, medicine, law, public administration and politics to develop a public which will not only homestead our new spaces in the sea but colonize and civilize them through an integrated interdisciplinary education in the sea-grant universities.

The fostering of such a spirit will become increasingly crucial. By focusing so intensely on agriculture the land-grant colleges often ignored other aspects of the land. Recreation, urban-land planning, open-space conservation, water-resources planning, and strip mines did not fare so well. The land-grant colleges sometimes failed to anticipate the larger significance of their agricultural practices; research stations popularized pesticides without always being aware of their full impact on the environment. Our present system of agricultural subsidies—bitterly criticized, reluctantly continued—testifies to the poverty of thought on the social and economic impact of agricultural affluence.

The sea-grant concept could fall into the same self-defeating specialization. "Scientific analysis, as necessary as it is, isn't all that we need," notes Dr. Stanley Cain, Assistant Secretary of the Interior. "We need synthesis of the information from many disciplines; we need to attack the systems as a whole." Such a vital synthesis can resolve heated resource conflicts, such as whales versus salt barges and kelp harvesters versus fishermen. Phenomenon such as the red tide can be unraveled in less than twenty years. Economical restraints can be placed on the new sea monster, the outfall. The necessity of persuading ocean users to coexist with one another and the ocean is intensifying daily; knowledge needs to be immediately available rather than laboriously assembled. Notes Abel, "We can forsee a major concentration of effort to use millions of acres of salt water marsh for aquaculture of several valuable marine food species—and we believe such an effort can provide a financial return that will compete with that now gained from filling our marshes to create building land. To preserve and utilize the marshes would be a major contribution to preserving the whole ecology of our estuaries and deltas."

A broad ocean comprehension can coordinate wasteful single-use projects into more economical multiuse projects. As the Institute of Marine Resources at the University of California observes, a harbor breakwater could be designed to accommodate shops, a seaward beach, subsurface tubes for utility and waste-disposal lines, and a roadway to an artificial island. Such an island might accommodate a nuclear reactor, a desalinization plant, an oil drill, a yacht mooring, and a boat landing. Such consolidation could also avoid the creation of a chain of navigational hazards.

The sea-grant system can explore and illuminate alternative trends in exploitation. What should be the proper balance between intense modification of ocean processes —akin to agricultural development of the land—and Dr. Odum's "utilization" theory of minimum intervention? How far should the ocean be partitioned into salmon, oyster, kelp, and wilderness areas? The chairman of the House Committee on Marine Fisheries, Congressman Edward Garmatz (Maryland-Dem.), proposes a ten million dollar program to eliminate stinging jellyfish "and other similar pests." Dr. Frank Johnson of Princeton now finds that the bather's stinging pest contains a rare substance that glows green in the presence of calcium. This luminous property can determine calcium levels in the human bloodstream, a prime indicator of parathyroid disorders. Sharks, another prime candidate for elimination, have an increasing food and hide value. A broader appreciation of the ocean will help us to classify ocean life into friends and pests.

A sea-grant synthesis of technology and politics will be particularly valuable. The United States's ability to influence ocean politics will depend less on Polaris subs than on knowledge that will foster full and peaceful utilization of ocean resources. Man may be able to reside in the sea, but if he has to hang plastic fish outside his tinted porthole the accomplishment dims.

A broad comprehension of the ocean alone will not protect it from the land's sometimes bitter fate, nor will it automatically inject harmony into the marine ambitions of twenty Federal agencies, twenty-five coastal states, and the other nations of the world. Such a broad comprehension, to be effective, must be reflected in public policy. Promising concepts like the sea-grant colleges thus serve as only one step, although an essential one. By approaching the ocean merely as a resource we foster conflict and eventual disaster. By approaching the ocean as an environment we can begin to meet the ultimate challenge: governing its anxious and ambitious exploiters.

11.

Hurrah's Nest

EVERY piece of land has its specific task, whether to provide corn, a tract pad, or a flood-control channel. The land that was once free has been meticulously, sometimes angrily, claimed, purchased, traded, litigated, annexed, zoned, and subdivided. Stand in wilderness, start walking, and you will soon encounter a bullet-riddled No Trespassing sign or an ingratiating forest ranger. The land's taskmaster is forever insinuating his presence.

Yet one area remains joyously free of such exclusive possession. On a body of water a fisherman may be fishing, a swimmer swimming, a dam damming, and the salmon, hopefully, running. A concept of "common" or "shared" use alien to that of the subdivided land functions here. This concept—access to most everybody, control to none—exploits the foremost value of a body of water, the remarkable sum of all its values. A Columbia River corporation which manufactures water power to the exclusion of fishing, irrigation, and sewage outfalls—except at a price—sounds preposterous. Lake Superior as a national sewage settling basin may appeal to hard-

139

pressed sanitary engineers but not to fisherman, Duluth power-boat squadrons, or to Canada.

A water body still comes under the control of government, but this control has been exercised with comfortable restraint. Traditionally, government's greatest interest in domestic waters has been a negative one—freedom of navigation; also the prevention of smuggling, gambling, or fish dynamiting. Within these bounds the shared-use concept regulates itself. Fishermen coexist with other fishermen as long as there is plenty of fish. Power-boat owners and sailboat owners may call each other "stick and string" sailors and "smudgepot sailors," but they still get along when there is plenty of room. Now, with today's undersea technology, two people may occupy the same general water space; a skindiver browsing below, a skiff skimming above. A boy in a rented dory has just as much right to row as a commercial fishermen to toss a net. There are no traffic lights. There are no cyclone fences. A river, lake, or ocean is an unspoiled place where nobody can trespass. You can turn left anywhere and keep going until you run out of gas or water. Is there any more relaxed feeling than to guide a boat away from a dock and realize that you are on your own, perhaps more so than in your own home?

Unfortunately, such self-regulation, however successful in the past, however appealing in the present, now jeopardizes the shared-use concept. The prerequisite—plenty of room—is breaking down under the pressures of congestion and depletion. A power boat cutting across the bow of a sailboat to make gleeful waves is one obvious sign of the breakdown. The pathetic riverbank line-up of hundreds of urban dwellers on the opening day of the trout season is another. The polluted condition of Lake Erie is still another. The Coast Guard now trailblazes "ship safety fairways" among the two thousand oil wells that stud the Gulf of Mexico. The modern waterway qualifies for the term once applied to confusion aboard a ship: a hurrah's nest.

A new, more aggressive concept of water use has

evolved. The owner of a cocktail lounge is painfully familiar with it; one happy victim of too many drinks can chase away the rest of the trade and have the bar all to himself. Bad manners, not ownership, beget control. Sewage districts and dam builders have been remarkably successful in applying this method to water use, oftentimes as unconsciously as the man at the bar.

The shared-use concept deteriorates into what might be termed "vulgarity control," as the drums beat ever louder for the ocean conquest. Today it is a concept badly in need of a referee, namely the Government, the traditionally restrained authority over water bodies. But government, at both the State and Federal level, faces a choice. Should the offshore waters, like the land, be parceled out and let to specific taskmasters? Tidelands and submerged lands can be leased for a variety of purposes from oyster farming to furnishing the underpinnings for new subdivisions. The ocean could be orderly, indeed: fish farms, oil fields, recreation preserves, machine-crafted isle chains, all crisscrossed by sea lanes (STAY OFF THE SHOULDER). People could trespass on water as well as on land, and the major trespasser would undoubtedly be the frivolous individual who dared to come down to the sea to enjoy it. He lacks the ticket of admission, a tax-producing activity. Is that not the best way to establish priorities of use? Who ever heard of running a farm as a playground?

On the other hand, government could seek to bring conflicting interests into harmony and thus reaffirm the utility of the shared use concept. However laudable, this goal might soon cause government to resemble a symphony conductor directing jazz soloists. Yet the politics to achieve such exacting harmony are already evolving in a marine region beset by extravagant use and abuse, the inevitable slum of most American cities—the waterfront.

The ocean is big, so big that it appears to have but one land bank, yet it remains kin to sweet-water lakes and brackish bays. All are bodies of water, filled with great promise and great frailty. Indeed, the lakes we call Great, and our grand ocean bays also, were once considered beyond man's power. Then work boots began scarring their shores; heavy machines began tamping, shoveling, pounding and spewing. Their noisy prostrations before the expanse of water seemed comical, yet a basic truth soon became appallingly evident. If you want to deprive yourself of everything a water body can offer, devour its shoreline. Devour the shore and you sever the heart of a water body and the spine of shared use. A body of water can lie within your power but, strangely enough, beyond your pleasure.

12.

Waterfront:
The Clear Reflection

In Chicago I reached that rewarding stage in boy-
hood in which I could swim over my head. And so I
would slip out of the hot summer and into Lake Michigan at will, lolling beyond the slight surf line, hearing
the muted chatter of picnickers, gazing at ore barges on
one horizon and, on the other, the skyscrapers, the bold
index fingers of urban wealth. It seemed quite natural
that picnickers, ore barges, Sunday fishermen, and boys
that swam out over their heads could coexist on a city
waterfront.

Only after leaving Chicago did I discover that the
common urban waterfront is hardly approachable, much
less swimmable, encrusted with wharves, switching yards,
sewage outfalls, and other industrial barnacles. It is the
true civic outcast, the ghetto of ghettos, familiar only to
longshoremen, sanitary engineers, and carp. "The divid-
ing line between land and water in our cities," notes
urban critic Walter McQuade, "is too often a creeping
smudge." Yet blue patches can tease the eye. Why, in

143

this day of urban renewal and water-pollution boards, must a waterfront with fifteen beaches, fifteen parks and not a single sewage outfall be so rare?

The question becomes all the more provoking when we realize that the Chicago waterfront was once as crass as its urban sisters. At the turn of the century the Chicago waterfront lay in industrial bondage. As a source of sewage disposal, its water had been stained by slag, tripe, tanning acids, metal pickling, and woodpulp excreted by the busy bowels of industry. As a transportation right-of-way, its tidelands had been shredded by railroad trestles. As a real estate reservoir, its shoreline had been pushed out of shape and buried. As an industrial bazaar, the buried shoreline accommodated steel plants bent on using the lake waters for cooling, sewage, and docking.

The reduction from living environment to industrial resource was accomplished under the best of intentions. The state, the owner of the lake tidelands, viewed them as any other public lands, to be let out to producers. There were eager enough developers—the Illinois Central Railroad, steel mills, and merchant princes seeking a private lake view. It became only natural to forfeit public control over the tidelands to achieve development.

The lakefront developed in the image of its exploitation, a muscular dullard, forever dumping cargo into holds and sewage into the water, always grunting, smoking, and smelling. The disappearance of the natural lakefront was a gradual process—occurring over some fifty years—and a nearly imperceptible one, concealed as it was behind a fence of railroad tracks and switching yards. The modern scouts of the outdoors, the pleasure seekers in outboards and snorkels, were yet to come. To people observing a six-day week and the Sabbath, the lake was generally viewed at a distance, and from there it looked much the same. Only on muggy summer days would it hint at its tattered condition. Odors like rotten eggs would seep through office buildings, homes, and the finer restaurants. Then the wind would shift and the odors diminish.

Some realized that more than sweet air was at stake. When the quest for productive development engulfed a lakeside park, a business iconoclast, A. Montgomery Ward, stormed, "They have made a dumping ground of the park, allowed circuses, naked bulls, and everything else. Here is park frontage on the lake, comparing favorably with the Bay of Naples, a breathing spot for the poor, which city officials would crowd with buildings." Others who shared Ward's disappointment felt that there was really no alternative. A city could no more afford a green lakefront in its midst than a pretty forest.

Yet one sturdy individual felt that the lakefront could perform industrial chores and, at the same time, be "the most attractive possible waterway and parkway ever known to man." The achievement of such coexistence was to become a matter of professional vindication for Daniel Hudson Burnham.

With a physique to match the rolling imperiousness of his name, Burnham could easily have been taken for the hard-driving, rough-hewn, self-made industrialist of the day. A hardy five-foot, eleven inch frame was topped with a bold face, piercing eyes, and a thick, virile mustache. He expounded ideas like a "railway locomotive under full steam, holding the right-of-way," according to one side-tracked admirer.

The man who so closely resembled an industrial tycoon was, in fact, an architect. In 1871 the Great Fire consumed Chicago. Horse teams dumped the smoking remains of eighteen thousand buildings into the customary dump, Lake Michigan. Architectural firms, including the young firm of Burnham and Root, were besieged with clients. In the heat of opportunity Chicago's architects not only rebuilt the city but evolved new technologies that allowed mundane office buildings to scrape the sky and overshadow church steeples. Between 1873 and 1890 Burnham and Root designed forty million dollars worth of buildings, from Bar Harbor to Mexico City.

In 1890 the firm was selected to design the World's Columbian Exposition to be held in Chicago three years later. John Root proceeded to design, while Burnham organized and constructed. The Exposition was to celebrate young America's rise to worldly prominence, but the site seemed hardly in keeping with the posturing. It was a piece of lake marshland somehow reprieved from industrial carnage. The site's damp, dreary character soon impressed itself on its would-be saviors. While touring the marsh during the winter, Root contracted a fatal case of pneumonia. Design responsibility for the Exposition's one hundred fifty buildings fell on Burnham.

In the largest cultural enterprise of the day Burnham supervised ten architectural firms, placated sculptors like Lorado Taft and Saint-Gaudens, and desperately cast about for a man who could transform the soggy Exposition site. The man turned out to be a New York landscaper, Frederic Law Olmstead. Gradually the marsh disappeared, to be replaced by lagoons and fountains, gardens and shady paths, a harmony of earth and water. This critical transformation gripped Burnham, gripped him with a power he could not fully comprehend at the time.

As the Director of Exposition Works, Burnham also supervised water drainage and electric power and approved of the presence of a giant revolving passenger wheel invented by a man named Ferris. The mobilized talent created a plaster world in which Pericles, if not Zeus, would have felt right at home. Only Louis Sullivan's Transportation Building, in maverick red and gold, mocked the classical craze of white columns, spouting fountains and fig-leafed statuary. Even the Temple of Vesta was reincarnated—as a chocolate booth.

To the public the Great White City was a symbol of what beauty was all about. To creative minds challenging old forms it was a disaster. "Grandomania," declared a young Frank Lloyd Wright. "Uncle Dan would have been equally great in the hat, cap, or shoe business." Sullivan, doomed to lifetime obscurity by the taste-setting Exposition, compared it with "horse-eagles, or pumpkin-bearing frogs, or tarantula-potatoes—the off-spring of an illegitimate commerce with the mongrel styles of the past. . . . Here one man's unbalanced mind spread a gauzelike pall of fatuity."

Gratified by the public recognition, perplexed by the professional derision, the Director of Works saw a new challenge. Rome, Paris, and other continental cities reflected a sense of beauty. If, in America, technical organization could routinely produce skyscrapers, railroad lines, Temples of Vesta, and other massive enterprises, why could it not shape that anarchistic form, the burgeoning industrial city? "I can see all America constructed along the lines of the Fair, in noble, classic, dignified style," Burnham told a bemused Wright. The human locomotive was ready to put the Great White City into production.

This was a bold vision in an age unacquainted with zoning commissions, city planning staffs, and high-rise hearings, but Burnham was only getting up steam. Olmstead's lagoons and garden islands had been carved out of marshland. Could not Chicago's entire eastern boundary—a twenty-five-mile lakefront gutter—be transformed into "the most attractive possible waterway and parkway ever known to man"? The lakefront was to become the proving grounds for Burnham's belief that an industrial city could shape its destiny in beauty and order.

On weekends, Burnham invited leading Chicago figures to his Evanston estate. Here, on a grassy esplanade flanked by elms and overlooking the blue lake, he lobbied tirelessly on behalf of his ambition. An invitation to speak in the mahogany den of the lakefront exploiters, the Merchant's Club, gave Burnham a chance to flex his persuasive muscles. He began, as Sullivan would have it, by "plastering them with flattery." "You are the men who have made Chicago, who have fought her battle, who have never been content to pause or rest." Yet a new battle awaited. "Looking toward the future, I suggest the time has come for Chicago to make herself attractive." Why attractive? "When a citizen is made to feel the beauty of nature, when he is lifted up by her to any degree above the usual drift of his thoughts and feelings, the state of which he is a part is benefited thereby."

Burnham then translated the benefits of beauty into his audience's native tongue: "Does anyone grown rich in the mines, the forests or the plains of our country come here to live or even linger for the sake of pleasure? Does he not pass through our city, remaining only as long as he is compelled to, so that we get the benefit neither of his money nor his presence among us?" Napoleon the Third installed tree-shaded boulevards and parks in Paris and look at the return on his investment. "I am told that the Parisians annually gain in profits from visitors more than the Emperor spent in making the changes." How to keep the money of visitors and residents alike in Chicago? Transform the lakefront. "Before us spreads a plantation of majestic trees, shadowing lawns and roadways, upon the margin of the lake. In contrast with it, the shining lagoons stretch away to the north. Now, can this dream be carried out? It rests with you."

Philip Armour and Marshall Field were ecstatic. George Pullman "took fire" and offered to dedicate his lakefront riparian rights to Burnham's vision. A potential enemy of lakefront restoration had become a fervid ally. But the city was unprepared to accept the challenge. The city's sewer system, Lake Michigan, would have to be replaced. Railroads and industry would have to be evicted from a shoreline the state legislature had granted away.

For the next decade Burnham commuted between Cleveland, Washington, San Francisco, Manila, and other cities more responsive to his visions of civic glory. In all these places Burnham attempted to anchor his plans to a restored and reopened waterfront. The city fathers, however, often became quickly disenchanted by Burnham's insistence on rolling back industrial sprawl, rerouting railroads, treating sewage, creating park systems—in short, approaching the city as a living environment rather than a working resource. That was fine for expositions but not for the world's fastest-growing industrial cities. Planning victories became holding actions at best. The reason a railroad does not run through the Washington Mall is that Burnham, as president of the Washington Plan Commission, stopped the Pennsylvania Rail Road from laying track at the risk of jeopardizing his own company's commission to design the Pennsylvania's Washington station.

All during this time Burnham was making water-color sketches of green parks and shining lagoons bordering on Lake Michigan, but the planning frustrations were beginning to tell. "Public work should be avoided by men who care for their own peace of mind," observed Burnham in 1904. At long last his home city was finding itself forced to indulge in some civic planning. In addition to functioning as an area of sewage disposal, Lake Michigan served as the city water supply. Continued outbreaks of cholera, dysentery, and typhoid indicated that the two uses conflicted and that continued extension of water intake pipes was not the solution. The lake that once just smelled now poisoned.

A sanitary engineer found that an eight-foot summit some twelve miles west of the lakefront prevented the Chicago River, which poured sewage into the lake, from draining into the Mississippi River system. The summit was breached and the Chicago River diverted to flow along a twenty-eight-mile canal to a Mississippi tributary. After pioneering earth-moving techniques that helped to construct the Panama Canal, Chicago started passing on its sewage problems to Joliet and other downstream communities. Yet storm runoff could still contaminate the lake and jinx the kitchen faucet. Chicago's subsurface was laced with intercepting storm drains. Today the American Society of Civil Engineers ranks this sewage system as one of the world's seven engineering wonders, right up there with the Panama Canal and the Empire State Building.

The summit leveling and ditch digging not only made the lake fit for drinking, it made it fit for swimming, boating, fishing, viewing, and shoreline planting . . . if access could be gained and public parks installed. In 1906 Burnham wrote to a friend, "I have now no connection with city planning except here in Chicago. This is absorbing me. It was undertaken as sort of a last campaign and because of a sense of obligation to my own city." The Commercial Club, successor to the Merchant's Club, had provided Burnham with a fifty-thousand dollar grant to realize his decade-old lakefront vision. Well aware of the limits of fine plans, Burnham immediately began mobilizing the public behind his last campaign. He set up his command post in the penthouse of the Railway Exchange Building (built by D. H. Burnham and Company). Bankers, artists, meat-packers, and ward politicians trooped to his offices and submitted to marathon luncheon-lectures. The human locomotive would set down his fork on a worktable and gesture toward the penthouse windows, which commanded an appalling view of the scarred lakefront. Then Burnham would point to sketches by his staff. "We see the broad water, ruffled by the gentle breeze; upon its breast the glint of oars, the gleam of rosy sails, the outline of swift gliding hulls. We hear the rippling of the waves, commingled with youthful laughter. A crescent moon swims in the western sky, shining faintly upon us in the deepening twilight." As the meat-packers and ward politicians left, Burnham would turn to his planning staff, a blend of engineers and skilled designers that foreshadowed the modern city planning office. "Make no little plans; they have no magic to stir men's blood. Let your watchword be order and your beacon be beauty."

Carried away by his own eloquence, Burnham expanded planning efforts to cover Chicago as well as the lakefront, including a system of scenic boulevards and forest preserves. He even sought to consolidate the sprawling system that continually defied his dreams of civic order, the railway facilities (Burnham, fortunately, was spared the sight of freeway intersections), but the lake remained the gilt-edge of planning. Refuse dumping had reclaimed lake frontage in the interests of steel plants and railroad trestles. Why not leap this industrial fence and create an entirely new lakefront with fill? The virgin area would lie securely in the public domain, beyond the monopoly of industry. Harbor sprawl would be compressed and made to coexist with fishing piers, beaches, bridle paths, marinas, and shining lagoons that would provide ice skating in the winter. Buildings would be permitted, but they would house museums, not just steel assembly lines, and they would be built to last! "No buildings of wood should be allowed anywhere on the entire system of boulevards, parks, and islands." As a promenade in keeping with the emerging auto age, Burnham added an outer shore drive, carefully set back from the beaches and parks.

After three years of penthouse luncheons Burnham distilled these concepts into the Chicago Plan. The leather-bound presentation, illustrated by a pair of artists imported from New York and Paris, clearly enunciated the natural and political character of the proposed new lakefront. "In its every aspect, the lake is a living thing, delighting man's eye and refreshing his spirit. Not a facet of its shores should be appropriated to individuals, to the exclusion of people." Declared Charles Eliot Norton, president emeritus of Harvard, "If the democracy of a great American city can comprehend and appropriate such a beneficent project as the 'Plan of Chicago' when put before them by a group of unusually intelligent and public-spirited citizens and can then get it well executed with promptness and prudence, it will be a good omen for the perpetuity of democratic institutions."

Primed by Burnham's last campaign, Chicago's mayor Fred Busse promptly formed the Chicago Plan Commission. In words with a familiar ring, the Mayor declared, "Making Chicago attractive to visitors from all parts of the world will add to Chicago's resources a very great commercial asset, the value of which will be reflected in every piece of real estate within our limits." A Burnham disciple of civic beauty, gruff beer baron Charles Wacker

chaired the Commission. "Frown upon unnecessary de-
lays," the Commission instructed the populace. "Hold
your representatives responsible for indifference and dila-
tory tactics." The Commission even made the Plan, soon
to become known as the Burnham Plan, part of the
school curriculum.

In 1912, well before his "noble diagram" could be
realized, Burnham succumbed to blood poisoning on a
European vacation. In a remarkable effort that continues
to this day Chicago has vindicated Burnham's vision.
The attempt to outflank the railroad with fill faltered,
for the Illinois Central claimed lakefront riparian rights.
After extended litigation, the railroad relinquished
claim to lake tidelands for recognition of its easement as
a property right. The way was clear for the monumental
fill project. To avoid damage suits from downstream
communities over sewage flows, Chicago treats its sewage
in multimillion dollar treatment plants. Burnham's shining lagoons tended to pond and stagnate lakefront
waters. Instead of lagoons peninsulas now curl out from
the shore, protecting boats on one side, beaches on the
other. Atop the artificial peninsulas sit parks and picnic
grounds. Chicago has spent more than three hundred
million dollars to regain and repair the lakefront that
the state legislature granted away.

This investment faces legal and political risks peculiar
to a waterfront. Although artificial beaches now outflank
the Illinois Central, the company still retains the railway
air rights that could possibly wall off the lakefront behind seventy-story buildings. Indiana, still holding a conventional view of the potential of a water body, allows
its steel plants to dump ammonia, cyanide, and "pickle
liquor" (acids to clean rust off metal) into the lake, an
intoxicating mixture that periodically haunts the Chicago beaches. (The Federal Water Pollution Control
Administration is presently applying pressures on Indiana steel plants.) Meanwhile, six Great Lake states and
Canada contest that Chicago has lowered lake levels and
endangered navigation by reversing the rivers that once

drained into Lake Michigan. (Russia is faced with a similar problem in the Caspian Sea, possibly because of irrigation diversions.) Chicago now faces an imposed ceiling on lake water diversion, and such a ceiling will increase reliance on expensive sewage treatment plants.

Chicago still does not regret its faith in the Burnham Plan. The industrial gutter is today a ribbon of blue water and green parks as wide as a mile. Each summer some seven million people flock from the steaming urban canyons to immerse themselves in waters that once reeked. Floodlights illuminate night swimming. Fishermen angle just beyond the shadow of skyscrapers, the din of traffic jams, and the sight of smokestacks. In other cities children go to summer camp and their parents travel to enjoy similar pleasures—if their incomes allow. The lake shore can provide an alternative to the breaching of corner fireplugs in the August heat.

Nonwood structures such as Shedd Aquarium, the Chicago Art Institute, the Museum of Science and Industry, and Soldier's Field grace this lakeside strip. Besides learning to swim on the lakefront, I became acquainted with Gershwin and Debussy at summer concerts in Grant Park, as the lake cooled the city and basked in its lights. Today, when I fly into Chicago, I see below me Burnham's vision and recall the memories that I once thought were common to any boy who lived in a city by the water.

The lakefront also supports two harbors, a convention center booked into the 1970's, a twenty-one-hundred-car parking lot, and a steel works. The harbors are efficiently compact and the parking lot lies below Grant Park. The McCormick Convention Center was granted a lakefront site because its depressed design precludes a scenic breakwater. U.S. Steel coexists with Calmut Beach.

Burnham's architectural tastes may have run to "tarantula-potatoes" and "horse-eagles," but his appreciation of and response to a shore environment reflects a much finer sense of harmony. Comprehensive planning of the shore—joined with clean water—can maintain the shared-use concept amid intense industrialization. Burnham's Chicago lakefront is the mirror lesson. The magnitude of this achievement can best be grasped by viewing the condition of the Great Lakes elsewhere. "Of all the Great Lakes cities," notes public health official LeRoy Scarce, "only Chicago has free use of all her beaches. Other large cities on the Great Lakes from time to time closed their beaches because of pollution." The billion-dollar defouling job of slimy Lake Erie may last for a decade before a child in Ohio, Pennsylvania, New York, and Canada's Ontario Province can safely learn to swim in its waters. A region with as much at stake in expanding marine capabilities thus finds its patrimony in a shambles. What good is the promise of fish farms, underwater parks, artificial beaches, and marine pharmaceuticals if the shore is barricaded and the waters lifeless?

Such shortsightedness is not limited to the Great Lakes cities. One metropolis has even degraded a grand ocean bay to the point that its future, as well as that of its surrounding region, stands in grave jeopardy.

13.

Waterfront:
The Cracked Reflection

AN ocean and a major river conjoin to form a minor sea inside the California coast. The Pacific enters through a milewide breach in stalwart bluffs. This breach, the Golden Gate, abruptly opens up like the wings of an enormous airliner to attain a span of some sixty miles and a width of as many as thirteen. The Sacramento River empties into the northern tip of the wing through secondary San Pablo and Suisun bays. Seamen like to boast that all the ships of the world could fit into the 435 square miles of San Francisco Bay.

This water body makes San Francisco and the other ninety communities in the Bay Area one of the world's most delightful urban regions. Many a city is beautiful only by night, when a million lights shimmer through the darkness that shrouds its asphalt flesh and iron bones, but San Francisco is beautiful by day as well, a geological mermaid that is part peninsula, part ocean bay; part skyscrapers, part sailing boats; part boulevards, part wharves; part library pigeons, part sea gulls; part green mountains and part blue plains. "The Bay," notes San Francisco Mayor John Shelley, "is the reason for San Francisco's existence."

Since 1850—the dawn of American civilization in California—people have been shoveling things into the bay to accommodate parking lots, supermarkets, a home for the San Francisco *Giants*, boatels, garbage dumps, and other additions to the property tax base. Today, as a result of this indiscriminate dumping, the Bay Area must enjoin itself from erasing the "reason for its existence." This is not merely a matter of aesthetics. It is a matter of such things as economy, climate, and health.

The patrimony of San Francisco Bay can be hard to grasp. Although Lake Michigan provides Chicago with a wonderful heritage, it by no means lies at the core of the city's existence. San Francisco's bay sets the city apart from any of its sister cities in America; it defines it uniquely and sets it to rank with the loveliest of the capitals of Europe. Its climate is softened by the bay waters—the summers cooled, the winters warmed. The city limits are a shoreline, not a sign, and the shoreline contains any number of small universes: sloughs, tule marshes, coves, beaches, creek mouths, all salt-smelling and tide-touched. Deep-draft channels bring Japanese tankers and other Pacific traders within blocks of the city center. Foghorns mourn above factory whistles. The city has a colorful fishing fleet—one that brings fresh salmon, bass, and oysters to the tables of wharf restaurants that cluster beside the bay. On weekends truck drivers catch a bus to join the commercial fishermen angling from piers.

A thousand waterfowl glide down from the sky. Geese banded in Siberia set down on the city's margin. Hens quack and drakes whistle. Diving ducks patter across the bay in takeoff. Red-breasted mergansers fly single file low to the water, and canvasbacks fly high in loose, fluttering V's. Collectors of seashells often pick up shotgun cartridges, for there are at least two hundred fifty duck clubs.

San Francisco seasons its food with salt from bay solar ponds. Schools and roads are built of cement made of blue clay and oyster shells skimmed from bay muds. The city plays host to honeymooners, Shriners, and international conferences. A city with a beautiful bay can charm the world.

San Francisco has a heritage of clipper ships, steamers, longshore riots, Jack London, port brothels, and tong wars. Here Captain Scammon rehired his crew to keep the whale lagoon a secret, only to be shadowed down the California coast by his peers.

The bay blesses San Francisco in many ways, but the sweetest of all is its mere presence. It constantly reappears to refresh the jaundiced urban eye, at street end, from hilltop, from a window—blue, open, airy—a sweep that no urban developer can subdivide, no shadowing skyscrapers can hide. Only the fog can do that.

This is San Francisco's unique patrimony, yet this is the same water body that the Bay Area finds itself almost compulsively destroying.

Like many other water bodies, San Francisco Bay does not flaunt its wounds. To the enchanted tourist sipping a scotch at the Top of the Mark the bay is very much there. Only as he gets closer to its edge does an oblique, rather fascinating hint suggest that the bay is in trouble. Drive along a freeway and you may see looming on the bayfront a skeletal dinosaur with an orange-crate head, a plywood warrior brandishing a garbage-can shield, and a hanging tree dangling a toilet-seat noose. Photos of "mudflat" or "derelict" art have been exhibited in Los Angeles and Colorado Springs as well. This native art form is based on the ingenuity of Bay Area artists and on the easy availability of junk flotsam.

This availability suggests that San Francisco Bay, like many other water bodies, is used as a garbage dump, only on a larger scale. Stone-pelted NO SWIMMING IN THE BAY signs confirm this. More than eighty outfalls discharge into the bay, their daily flow rate equaling that of a river. Pioneer Rubber, Dow Chemical, the U.S. Naval Magazine, San Quentin Prison, and the City of San Francisco all relieve themselves in this manner. There is a reluctance to complicate this simple form of disposal. It took a court order to encourage San Francisco to upgrade its sewage treatment in accord with minimum state requirements.

"To be immersed in bay waters today," says urban critic Allan Temko, "is to risk having one's skin peel from the body." This peril can inhibit sailing as well as swimming. Pollution has long since purged the oyster beds Jack London once raided. The daily bay diet now includes two hundred thirty-nine pounds of chromium, one hundred seventy-two pounds of copper, and sixty tons of oil and grease. San Francisco's fishing fleet must go out to sea to make a living. Sport fishermen still fish the bay waters but their livelihood does not depend on the striped bass and starry flounder they manage to hook.

The Bay Area is no more heedless than other regions in recruiting its waterfront as a sewage disposal. Its real callousness is revealed in its exploitation of bayside land. Reclaiming a body of water for the land can be expensive. Holland reclaims the Zuider Zee and Japan reclaims Tokyo Bay by diking off a water area and then draining it. The "polder" method can run about one thousand dollars an acre. Yet San Francisco Bay is being reclaimed by the fill method, which runs upward of twenty-seven thousand dollars an acre. Polder land is generally restricted to agricultural and recreational purposes. Filled land can accommodate industrial and commercial uses. The demand for reclaimed land with a marine view is so high that its price can escalate to sixty thousand dollars an acre, twice the cost of reclamation. Such potential profit should temper doubts about the financial feasibility of reclaiming the crucial estuaries of the Gulf of Mexico. Inevitably, large chunks of the Gulf itself and the shallow Atlantic offshore will become candidates for reclamation.

The state also permits tideland developers, private and public, to form reclamation districts and pass long-term bonds to finance the high initial cost. With financial incentives like this there is little motivation for building artificial peninsulas that curl out from the shore to protect public beaches on one side and public marinas on the other. There is, in fact, no motivation at all for preserving the natural shoreline.

The resulting tideland rush creates its own unique problem: a critical need for fill. San Mateo County, planners of a twenty-three-square mile fill called Foster City, are even considering the nearby San Bruno Mountains as a solution. ("Dumping the hills into the bay doubtless would be hailed as a great engineering achievement," chides naturalist Harold Gilliam. "All that remains is for someone to suggest that it be done with nuclear energy—all at once.") The demand for fill solves another pressing problem. Because the Bay Area leaves little room for garbage dumps and smog regulations frown on incineration, Golden Gate Disposal, Sunset Scavenger Corporation, and other aptly named firms gladly pay for the privilege of dumping garbage onto municipal tidelands. The resulting sanitary fill can become a hotbed of odors. Often on a hot summer day an acquisitive contractor will suggest that the time has come to reclaim the "stinking mudflats" as a shopping center, housing tract, or other improved form of tax revenue. Golden Gate Disposal et al. then move in to qualify another tideland for stinking mudflat status.

If the Bay Area, like Chicago, had to drink from its waterfront, this sort of exploitation might have been challenged sooner. As it was, the question of the bay's destiny was first raised in the form of suggestion by a knowledgeable outsider. In a city plan he drew up for San Francisco at the behest of the Crockers, the Hopkinses, and the Phelans, Daniel Hudson Burnham said, "There should be piers for public recreation, a yacht and boat harbor, and vast bathing places, both enclosed and open-air. People will seek the Outer Boulevard and will find refreshment and benefit from the water frontage." The day before the plan was to be distributed, the earth trembled and San Francisco was engulfed by the earthquake and fire. The plan was never distributed.

A half century and many fills later, Mrs. Clark Kerr, wife of the then president of the University of California, was accustomed to escorting the Queen of Greece, Britain's Prince Philip, and other distinguished visitors to the Bay Area. Mrs. Kerr found herself repeatedly apologizing for the pungent condition of the bayfront and soon discovered that other residents were similarly distressed. The "Save the Bay Association" was formed and swiftly attracted four thousand members, including Fleet Admiral Chester Nimitz (ret.), newspaper publisher Joseph Knowland, photographer Ansel Adams, and former National Park director Newton Drury.

The Association suspected that the sanitary fills, the reclamation projects, the dredging, and the sewage discharges were getting altogether out of hand, but there was really little public knowledge of the bay other than its fill specifications. Professor Mel Scott of the University of California's Institute of Governmental Studies was commissioned to look at the bay as a regional entity. His report, "The Future of San Francisco Bay," confirmed the suspicions of the Association.

On a biological level the fill operations were systematically burying the sedge, the smartweed, the eelgrass, and the bulrushes that succor waterfowl and make the duck clubs possible. The dump trucks of Golden Gate Disposal were burying the juicy muds whose minerals and nutrients fed the shrimp and worms on which salmon and flounder fatten. Such burials would ultimately narrow suitable bird habitats to telephone power lines and rotted pier pilings, perches not conducive to sheltering canvasbacks and Siberian geese.

On the recreational level bay development was fostering a unique and unwitting law violator. If a resident allows himself to be drawn by the traditional magnetism of water and he succeeds in crossing Bayshore Freeway, the Southern Pacific railroad tracks, the dumps and factory parking lots, he will reach water's edge only to be, most probably, a lawbreaker, guilty of trespassing on private lands. Of the two hundred seventy-six miles of bayfront, a mere five are in developed parks. With a water boundary ten times smaller, Chicago's parks provide five times as much water frontage.

At a public health level fill operations were constricting tidal currents and the tidal turbulence that fosters recreation. The bay's ability to absorb mammoth wasteloads was being paralyzed, particularly in the South Bay. "It is just as though you took a tub of water and rocked it," observes Bernard Smith, a Corps engineer. "The water just goes up and down but there is not so much translatory motion as there is in the North Bay. Also, of course, by unlucky coincidence, the greater part of the population is concentrated on the South Bay, where you get the heavy effluent from San Jose and Redwood City." The tides were still strong enough, however, to swirl into sanitary fills and leach out pollutants and toilet-bowl seats, tires, orange crates, and other materials necessary for the pursuit of mudflat art.

The constricted tidal prism also decreases the bay's ability to scour channel-clogging silt and thus increases harbor dredging efforts. The Corps of Engineers must often dump its unwanted silt in a hundred-foot hole near the Golden Gate egress. Outgoing tides sweep some of it into the Pacific, but seventy per cent returns to the navigation channels on the wings of the incoming tides. "We're merely pushing dirt around," one dizzied engineer told Professor Scott.

Fill operations can also prevent storm and sewage drainage from running into the bay by causing it instead to back up into the cities. Filled land, particularly when nudged by earth tremors (a not uncommon occurrence in the Bay Area), can settle all too abruptly and thus render reclamation bonds delinquent. Like beach engineering, fill engineering often reveals a self-defeating quality.

The unfortunate side effects of fill operations led to concern with their pace. Since General Stephan Kearny, military governor of the Territory of California, put Yerba Buena Cove to bid, a third of the original bay—two hundred fifty-seven square miles—has been filled in. Are there any natural limitations on such a land rush? Approximately seventy per cent of the remaining 435 square miles of bay is eighteen feet or less in depth, technically as easy to fill as a grave. Despite its immense sweep, San Francisco Bay is nothing but a large, shallow reflecting pool cut through by a deep river channel. Left uncontrolled, fill operations could shrink the bay into a river. Nicholas Petris of Oakland, a state legislator with an interest in the bay's future, suggested that Bay Area hills may eventually overlook "a bay full of tract housing, supermarkets, filling stations, hamburger stands, and factories." (The opportunity for such an overview may be limited if the San Bruno Mountains wind up in the bay.) Factors other than the view would be affected. Flood and sewage problems would be vastly magnified, valley smog would replace bay fog, and wharfage would be compressed into a riverfront.

All these present and future evils were being fostered in the name of alleviating a land shortage, but, as the Association discovered, the real shortage appeared to be in planning. Corps studies disclosed that there is enough suitable nonbay land to absorb fourteen million people in the Bay Area and still leave thirty per cent of the land undeveloped. The present population of the Bay Area is four million.

The various bay communities have zoning control over private tideland development and full control over their own tideland grants from the state. Here was authority enough to reverse the trend of bay development. Yet each city regarded the continuance of such a trend as vital to its future development and prosperity. Nobody, the Association was told, ever intended to bury the bay.

"It's still there, isn't it?" asked one city manager, pointing out his window.

The Association went to the next level of government, the state. As usual, they discovered the various state commissions working industriously at cross-purposes. They found that the State Highway Commission was planning bayfront freeways that the State Fish and Game Commission felt might entomb critical wildlife habitat; but Fish and Game officials were hampered by lack of adequate staff and funds to suggest less destructive routes to the Highway Commission. The State Water Quality Control Board was trying to upgrade bay sewage disposal at the same time that the State Port Authority was dumping raw sewage into the bay. The State Lands Commission, responsible for seeing that municipal tideland grants were used in the "general statewide interest," had no definition of this interest. (At the city level a similar chaos obtained. One city need not even confer with its neighbors on projects of mutual interest. Airport fill operations intensified sewage disposal problems of two cities nearby.)

The Association went next to the Federal Government. There they found an agency that not only viewed the bay as a regional entity but had the technical expertise to document its views. The Corps of Engineers had a simulated model of the bay to help in its supervision of bay navigation. Based on model studies associated with this responsibility, Corps planner Bernard Smith declared, "The Corps of Engineers places the problem of pollution of San Francisco Bay in the category of extreme and immediate urgency." The Corps also recognized another problem. "Now when you fill the Bay you reduce the tidal prism and in reducing the tidal prism you have reduced the strength of the tidal currents," observed Smith.

The Corps also possesses the authority to implement its knowledge. It has to approve fill permits, but even though it recognizes that pollution is of "immediate urgency" and that fill operations directly hamper channel clearance operations it also feels that its statutory authority limits disapproval to islands in the middle of channels and other obvious navigational hazards.

The Save the Bay Association was faced with a hurrah's nest of fine perfection. The bay as a bay did not exist, legally speaking. It existed only as a real estate reservoir, a transportation right-of-way, or a cesspool. Professor Scott suggested that a new political instrument be formed. A Bay Conservation and Development Commission would plan the bay as a regional resource and would be empowered to veto fill projects.

In 1963 Assemblyman Petris of Oakland introduced a bill that embodied these concepts, including sharp restrictions on fill operations. The subsequent opposition to the Petris bill illustrates the sort of myopia a body of water can inspire. Two entirely different shorelines suddenly emerged. Where the Bay Association saw the key to the bay's biological and recreational values, developers and city managers saw "ugly mud sloughs." "I don't know of any responsible businessman who's against conservation," explained Charles Travers, president of Reclamation District 2087 and manager of some one thousand tideland acres owned by Utah Construction and Mining Company. "But if you're trying to conserve mudflats or mosquito-ridden marshlands, that's not conservation." Travers then went on to describe protectors of mosquito-ridden marshlands as "drumbeating ladies and bird watchers," a novel description of Fleet Admiral Nimitz and Oakland publisher Joseph Knowland.

Assemblyman Carl Britschgi, who identified himself as author of a bill that transformed bay tidelands into a little league ballfield, proposed a redefinition to resolve the two divergent shoreline views. Shoreward limits of the bay, the high-tide mark, should be set back to the low-tide mark. This redefinition legislates out of existence the tidal region and anticipates the bulkheading of the Pacific and Atlantic coasts. It is a redefinition that is too easily suffered in practice.

Most critical testimony was confined, however, to the

alleged consequences of the Petris bill. Airport officials declared that fill restrictions would put San Francisco "out of business as far as jets are concerned." To avoid noise suits the airport has simply extended runways out into the bay. (Meanwhile, on the other side of the bay, the Oakland Airport is busily extending its runways, which leads to humorous speculation that the two systems will meet and provide the only municipal runway long enough for the supersonic airliner.)

The testimony of the Dredging Contractors Association was, as might be expected, lively. B. E. Peterson of the Association said the Petris bill served to "personally insult" local project planning. "Concern for the effects on the tidal prism on what filling might be done by private interests during the next four years is an emotional absurdity." Peterson then proposed his candidate for the bay's real villain, the state highway commission, with its plans for paving under the bayfront. Concluded Peterson, "Please understand, we enthusiastically endorse regional planning." (Commented one state legislator, "I didn't know whether you were a dredging contractor or a pile driver from the weight with which you hit some of these problems.")

San Mateo County, still planning to install Foster City in the bay, with or without mountains, provided a display of unenlightened self-interest. San Francisco had its turn in filling the bay, *now* it was San Mateo's. Summarized County Manager T. E. Stallings, "To place a moratorium on any bay fill activities within the boundaries of San Mateo County would set back the economic and recreational development of this county for at least ten years." Only one civic voice dissented from such reasoning. "Decisions concerning the bay's shoreline cannot be left entirely to individual communities because what each community does to the bay affects not only itself but its neighbors as well," testified Paul Micou, Mayor of Sausalito—a charming, artistic and residential community which faces complete exclusion from the bay by fills emplaced by a northern neighbor.

Such testimony, more than any statements by the Bay Association, confirmed the possibility of bay burial. "You know," remarked one state legislator, "it is fortunate that there is not enough dirt around here to fill up the Pacific Ocean." The legacy of a century had come home to roost. The Bay Area could ensure its future well-being only by sharply curtailing practices considered vital by prominent and well-intentioned interests. Civic officials and bay property holders such as Utah Construction and the Southern Pacific Railroad lobbied vigorously against the Petris bill. The Bay Association cultivated the support of the local press, citizen and sport groups, and the academic community. Declared poet Josephine Miles in the pages of *Atlantic Monthly:*

> Saving the bay. Saving the blasted bay.
> That there be margins of the difference
> Scrap heap and mobile, wind ridge and ledge,
> Rockfish and silverside, channel and tide,
> Mud and debris. That there be
> Shore and sea.

The Petris bill did not even get out of committee, but San Francisco State Senator Eugene McAteer, who once supported a controversial dredge-and-fill project in the bay, decided to coauthor a new bill with Petris. A committee chairman, torn between sympathy for the bill's intent and the realization that Utah Construction held potentially valuable tidelands in his bay district, persisted in holding up the bill. After much cajoling, it finally reached the legislative floor. The bill Bay Area cities almost unanimously dreaded was unanimously adopted by the lower house of the state legislature. A little bit of perspective can go a long way in matters of marine conservation. Utah's Mr. Travers was reduced to citing the legislation as "just another trend or drift in the socialistic direction."

The Bay Conservation and Development Commission

has gone on to prepare a master plan "treating the Bay as a body of water, not as real estate." The plan recommends ways to carefully control and limit commercial, residential and industrial use of bayfront to essential uses. Some 7,400 waterfront acres would be set aside for shoreline parks, beaches, fishing piers, scenic drives, bike paths and wildlife preserves. Fill projects would be kept to a minimum; the Commission, using its interim power over fill projects, limited filling to 110 acres in a three-year period. The Commission urges that a permanent government agency be established to accomplish the plan; the State Legislature is presently considering this proposal. While generally well-received, Commission recommendations still face formidable hurdles. On the sidelines stand the Santa Fe and Southern Pacific railroads, Utah Construction, Wells Fargo Bank, and other far-sighted corporations who quietly acquired much of the private tidelands the state has so eagerly disposed of. Today state holdings in the bay have shrunk to lands beneath the deep-draft channels. Private owners hold about half the reclaimable lands, bay cities the other half under state grants. Corporations are prone to institute lawsuits over any zoning ordnances they consider condemnation without compensation. Well-financed referendum campaigns can repeal legislative measures considered harmful to the interests of stockholders. "Vote No Against Mudflats by Voting Yes on Proposition More Land" may well pop up on bayfront billboards. As Chicago discovered, a corporation on just one part of the shoreline can influence the character of the entire shoreline.

The Commission may come up with an attractive plan that will inspire necessary public support but will be useless unless another problem is solved. Since 1949 a regional water pollution board has been seeking to remove No Swimming signs. Although two hundred million dollars has been expended on sewage treatment facilities and the Port Authority has finally hooked its outfalls into such a facility, the ultimate solution may be a massive sewage aqueduct to the Pacific Ocean. (Such a solution would deprive marine organisms in the bay of one outfall benefit; the fresh-water inflow helps to retard deadly salt-water intrusion.) The Pacific may also be recruited to solve the problem of putting four million pounds of Bay Area refuse out of sight daily if Golden Gate Disposal finds tidelands closed to sanitary fill. Meanwhile, an agency of the Federal Government may emulate Indiana's behavior on the Lake Michigan waterfront. The Federal Bureau of Reclamation plans to drain ten thousand acre-feet of farmland effluent into the bay annually. This effluent will contain sodiums, pesticides, sulfates, and slime-forming nitrates. The request by a state pollution official for "valid evidence that the price of the drainage system will not include the degradation of San Francisco Bay" was termed irresponsible by the state's Director of Natural Resources.

Chicago has already spent a half century in rectifying the waterfront policies of a state legislature that convened a century ago. The spiralling demands of waste generation also haunt efforts to rescue the bay. Merely purifying the tainted bay will not be enough. This magnificent water body has been a crude escape hatch from civic responsibility in sewage disposal, transportation routing, land use, and, in general, public planning. The region must reform its entire response to the natural world it lives in. Only then will the dangers that the sickly bayfront poses to the health, economy, and the very existence of the Bay Area subside. Once the shore is revived, the waters will spring back to life, ready to feed, entertain, cool, cure, and refresh. The goal of shared water use will always vindicate its supporters.

Tools of civic uplift that Burnham never dreamed of —urban renewal and the Federal Water Pollution Control Agency—are helping to spark similar waterfront projects in Boston, Philadelphia, St. Louis, Louiville, and other concerned cities. As in Chicago and the Bay Area, most of these waterfront projects are committed to the demanding challenge of shared use, but some

appear to lack the public vision that Burnham so earnestly cultivated. Into a hundred-acre project Boston is
cramming a townhouse complex, a motor hotel, a yacht
club, a shopping center, a restaurant wharf, and a park.
(How did that manage to slip in there?) This is certainly
shared use but in an ominous, commercial sense. Washington, D.C., obligingly set aside a waterfront site for
apartments "designed expressly for those whose professional stature, social standing, or personal achievement merit true distinction in living" (heated garages,
woodburning fireplaces, and musical elevators). Such an
exclusive trend could foster a shoreline as segregated
as its grimy industrial forebear, walled off by luxury
apartments, and encrusted with fish-wharf restaurants,
convention blockhouses, and expense-account gift shops.

The promise of shared use is only now dawning on
the American waterfront, and a prerequisite to its attainment becomes the salvaging of a butchered shoreline. Now comes the challenge of the coastal ocean and
of a marine technology that would pale Poseidon. Here
is an opportunity to seize or to ignore.

14.

To Lose the Ocean

Two decades ago the Supreme Court declared that the Federal Government owned the lands beneath the territorial sea of the United States. So vigorously did the coastal states lobby against this decision that the Congress finally ceded to the states the marine lands of this three-mile sea. (The Court, because of historical grants, ruled that Texas and the Gulf side of Florida possess the seabed out to three marine leagues, more than eleven miles.) In the "battle of the tidelands" the coastal states were inspired largely by the prospect of offshore oil royalties. Now they must face up to the real consequences of their lobbying. Theirs is a major responsibility to see that offshore oil fields, artificial islands, submotels, breakwaters, mining scoops, and other aspects of the ocean conquest do not transform our coastal frontier into a giant replica of the unsightly urban waterfront.

California fronts on twelve hundred miles of ocean. The state is generally noted for the advanced practices of its government, and a number of its agencies are active in the marine area: the Fish and Game Commission, the Water Quality Control Board, the State Lands

Commission, and the Division of Beaches. California would seem to be a good indication of the emerging ability of states to protect their shores. In this regard the University of California's Institute of Marine Resources notes the following in "California: The Uses of the Ocean":

> Rational planning of the shoreline is urgent. . . . Multipurpose planning and development of the coastline will be necessary if optimal use is to be made of the coast as a resource. There is no rational and systematic method by which the concerns of the general public related to the aesthetic and the hazardous aspects of new technologies is considered by the planning and regulatory agencies of the state.

It is of some comfort that this report was financed by the state government, the target of its criticism. The other twenty-nine states that border the ocean and the Great Lakes tend to show very little interest in rationality. No state has really attempted to survey and inventory the values of its marine frontier. No state has envisioned a comprehensive plan in the Burnham tradition that would fulfill the promise of many of these diverse values. Tidelands are still granted to local governments with few guidelines other than those concerning retention of mineral rights. No state has really attempted to set up an authoritative agency like the Bay Conservation and Development Commission which can view marine exploitation with some objectivity. Thus California's Fish and Game Commission tries to protect the kelp forests from outfalls approved by its Water Quality Control Board. Florida passes legislation to enable local governments to set aside estuaries, whereas local governments show more interest in reclaiming them. A hurrah's nest of grand proportions, fully capable of clouding the vital perspective provided by the sea-grant colleges, may thus evolve. At times the states appear to repose their faith in the existence of that mermaid who appears miraculously to unsnarl hazards with a flick of her fishtail.

The Federal Government retains the seabed of the continental shelf beyond the three-mile limit. This considerable piece of property extends a hundred miles or more off the mid-Atlantic shore. Alaska and Florida border continental shelves the equal of their land size. The Federal Government also retains navigation and other interests in all domestic waters. Some twenty-two bureaus, five departments, and three independent agencies exercise these interests. At the Congressional level some thirty-two authorization and appropriation committees find themselves reviewing portions of this administrative deployment.

The number of agencies involved might suggest a comprehensive grasp of ocean affairs; unfortunately, a Federal hurrah's nest is the result. The Navy unintentionally booby traps valuable seabeds administered by the Department of the Interior, which, with the co-operation of Gulf states, has approved oil drill islands that make the Gulf of Mexico a hazard to navigation. The Corps of Engineers excavates estuaries for deep-draft vessels, but the Bureau of Commercial Fisheries earnestly seeks their preservation. The Department of Defense meanwhile has set aside sixteen million acres of the California offshore, including three islands, for ship-to-shore bombardment and other exercises, thus causing the offshore oil industry to speculate on when and where this acquisitiveness will end.

In 1966 the Congress authorized a Commission on Marine Science, Engineering and Resources to investigate ways to coordinate and consolidate national ocean activities. Congress also established the National Council on Marine Resources and Engineering Development, composed of the Vice President and cabinet-level officers. This Council will be in a good position to combat restricted ocean vision, and it may involve setting up a Department of Marine and Atmospheric Affairs, as suggested by Senator Edmund Muskie (Maine-Dem.). The Council, however, may find this separation of land and marine responsibilities too drastic (i.e., need there be a Bureau of Land Mines and a Bureau of Marine Mines?) and may conclude that ocean activities, unlike agriculture, cannot be consolidated into one department and two legislative committees. An effective means of Federal coordination must eventually be established; otherwise the trustee of the coastal ocean will continue to preside over a maritime circus. (The trustee presently receives more in submarine oil royalties than it invests in oceanographic research. If this trend continues, we may witness the makings of an absentee landlord on the continental shelf.)

An improved Federal orientation toward the ocean will become especially important for coastal states as they, hopefully, broaden their own view of their ocean border. An appreciation of the ocean becomes useless without the technical resources to put it into practice, and states must depend on considerable Federal assistance. The national sea-grant college system is one move in this direction. Mapping and surveying work by the Coast and Geodetic Survey will help familiarize states with the seabeds they control. On the biological level Senator Gaylord Nelson (Wisconsin-Dem.) proposes Federal support of ecological surveys that would inventory both land and water environments.

However, the problem of implementing such a broad ecological perspective, a perspective that could foster this planet's first large-scale application of environmental management remains. The National Council on Marine Resources and Engineering has formed a Committee on Multiple Uses of the Coastal Zone "concerned with the broad areas of environmental planning, conservation and development including erosion control . . . conservation of marine ecology and recreational development of marine areas and pollution abatement and control in bays, estuaries and the Great Lakes." The Committee includes officials from Interior, State, Commerce, Transportation, National Science Foundation, Atomic Energy Commission, Defense, Smithsonian Institution and Council of Economic Advisers. The Committee, at present, has no powers beyond recommendation and its initial activities are largely limited to a pilot program of coordination in Chesapeake Bay. Yet the future significance of this Committee might be better imagined if a

Committee on Multiple Uses of the Land and Air had been formed by President Washington after crossing the Potomac near an outfall.

Coastal states are finally beginning to form similar committees. In California, an advisory Commission on Marine and Coastal Resources is attempting to prepare a comprehensive ocean program. Both California and Florida have even appointed commissions to recommend criteria and sites for a chain of statewide marine parks. Two Southern California communities, Newport Beach and Laguna Beach, have arranged for preserve status to revive rocky shores whose marine life has been ravaged and ransacked by crow bars and teardrops of paralyzing nicotine.

While heartening, this broadening of political perspective is often not accompanied by any broadening of representation. For instance, many of the state and federal commissions being established to plan marine programs are often a collection of various resource interests. However, coastal residents, local officials, recreation and conservation interests and education representatives have just as much at stake in these planning and policy-making processes and their representation should exceed tokenism. The polluted Los Angeles Inner Harbor has been compared to an old refrigerator in its ability to lure young fish schools to their death. The resulting fish kills have been condoned by the Los Angeles Regional Water Quality Board, whose members include the most notorious harbor polluters. This membership is justified on the basis that companies using the harbor as a sink have the most expertise in water quality matters.

Largely through the efforts of the Board's one member-at-large, Mrs. Ellen Stern Harris, state legislation is pending to broaden public representation. The frustrating inability of citizens to protect their environment from private and public agencies was highlighted at a congressional hearing in 1968. The House Subcommittee on Oceanography was considering a proposed marine sanctuary. Testified a resident, "Oil rights must not be permitted to obliterate the rights of Americans to enjoy uncluttered ocean views, unpolluted seascapes and beaches and unimpaired fisheries. A series of residential communities that have been conscientous about zoning on shore are shocked to find themselves powerless to insist on zoning and other orderly balanced development principles of planning allocation of uses offshore." An Interior official, successfully opposing the sanctury proposal, testified, "The willingness of the oil and gas industry to bid $603 million for drilling and production rights indicates the potentially large oil deposits that underlie the channel area . . . Every effort has been made to place specifications on these operations so that they will be conducted with a minimum of impact on other values in the channel." Seven months later, the area in question—the Santa Barbara Channel in Southern California—was treated to the Union Oil offshore blowout that more than justified the concern of the resident, Fred Eissler, also a Sierra Club director. Inadequate well casing and ill-understood geological fissures turned the blowout into a 800-square-mile oil slick that smeared sand and rock shores. Such episodes make an increasingly strong case for the need of commissions with an ecological competence enpowered to pass judgment on coastal resource decisions, particularly on appeal from citizen groups.

Public ownership of the shore, as well as ecology, can be subverted by resource-obsessed decisions. In many coastal states, the public owns the shore up to the mean high tide line. A mile from my Southern California home is a modest cradle of the sea called Upper Newport Bay. A New Town developer who should know better, Irvine Company, has proposed a land trade of private uplands for public tidelands in order to reclaim the bay shore for real estate. The staff of the California State Lands Commission warned the trade "would convert public waterways into a captive waterway primarily for the use of private residential boat owners who would occupy the created area and dominate the bay." Vertical bulkheads tend to make the public's ownership of the shore up to the mean high tide line rather meaningless:

public footholds along the "captive waterway" would largely be limited to flood control and storm drain outlets. However, the Commission has approved the trade. As a result, the last substantial estuarine environment in Southern California is tentatively doomed. (The tidelands trade is presently being challenged in the courts by a Los Angeles lawyer, Ralph Perry. At the same time, a citizens group, Friends of Newport Bay, has been bringing the bay's plight to public attention through the medium of environmental tours that have been attracting up to 1,500 people.)

The ability of public authorities to be seduced by handsome, private "master plans" for shore development is all too common on the Atlantic Coast as well as the Pacific. Ultimately, access to much of America's shore may be restricted to people who own pleasure boats or who live in shore estates guarded by electric gates with NO TRESPASSING signs. Such a trend would mock the efforts of earlier, less-affluent generations to set aside public shoreline for we of the present generation. Oregon has adopted the policy of acquiring for the public the shoreline up to the 16-foot elevation, well into the "dry sand" zone. Daniel Hudson Burnham would be mightily impressed. This is far-sighted public management at its best.

Conservation and environmental groups across the country are now pushing for such management vigorously. In California, the Planning and Conservation League is preparing to push for a Southern California Corridor Commission to effect public and ecological enhancement. The American Catecean Society has used blimps to take census counts of gray whale migrations and spot pollution plumes from outfall discharges. On the East Coast, the American Littoral Society, with a grant from the Conservation Foundation, has published an outstanding review on estuaries, *Fish and Man* by John Clark, and established an estuarine alert system to spot harmful exploitation at an early date. The plight of our estuaries will provide a crucial test in the race between heedless exploitation and rational development. Recent court decisions restrict the Corps of Engineer's ability to balance ecological values with navigation values in issuing bay dredging permits. If a Congressional remedy is not forthcoming, we will eventually forsake the sea's nurseries and help sterilize both the offshore and the skies above. The changeover from sloping shore to concrete bulkhead would, of course, benefit one living creature. If you are a barnacle, the muscular conquest of the ocean promises many spacious perches.

With the ocean being prepared for exploitation as meticulously as a patient for an operation, the need for comprehensive public management becomes even more urgent. Technology is being developed not only to allow us to farm and ranch the sea but to fertilize entire ocean regions, perhaps by inducing upwelling with seafloor nuclear heaters. Technology will soon begin to "stretch" shorelines by dredging out artificial coves and using the spoil to create artificial islands.

As in the San Francisco Bay Area, there are plans afoot to deter airplane noise by extending supersonic runways out into the Pacific Ocean and the Great Lakes. There are plans to dam Long Island Sound and other estuaries as fresh-water reservoirs to quench water shortages and to "fence" fish behind curtains of bubbling air or electrical impulses in order to cultivate them for the dinner table. Excess heat from coastal atomic power plants may be put to work to foster year-round ocean bathing. Such schemes, some speculative, some under serious consideration, are exciting, provocative, and of enormous potential benefit. Yet their by-products—upset ecology, pollution, habitat destruction, and distorted currents—are nightmarish. Unless government can relate these plans to one another and to the ocean, a technological horror show could ensue. A government equipped to coordinate such activities can also foster the multipurpose breakwaters and artificial islands that sea-grant colleges may design. An example of successful multipurpose project planning may be provided by the aerospace industry—the industry that successfully interlocks complex space technology with systems management. Government may find it feasible to put this experienced managerial capability to work as consultants on coordinating complex ocean activities.

The visions of a Jules Verne are now being presented to us as everyday choices, yet they must be carefully made, for each time we choose, we will, in a larger sense, be opting for a Chicago or a San Francisco waterfront. The ultimate folly is to endow technology with but one eye for one special interest. One-eyed ocean technology cripples all, but it is absolutely fatal to rather modest ocean users. Swimmers and scuba divers can no more exist in fouled, muddy waters than sardines or whales. In the past government has often played a negative role in shaping the use of the land. Today, as the only property holder in an environment that requires shared rather than exclusive use, government can no longer remain passive. This, of course, does not require nationalization of the offshore oil industry or the enlistment of fishermen in the civil service. Government's role in the future will be to relate rather than conduct development. The more vigorously and thoroughly government prepares for this demanding role the more likely it will be to find itself in the business of protecting, rather than salvaging, the coastal environment.

15.

The Queen, the Dutchman *and* Mare Liberum

SOVEREIGN authority is the sole issue that does not arise in a discussion of the development of the coastal ocean; the fishermen, the oilmen, the sanitary engineers, and other users are not questioning—much less denying —the right of the Federal or state government to lay down rules of conduct. Yet on the high seas, which constitute three fourths of the world's surface, this issue crops up increasingly. Although ostensibly at once *res cullius* (belonging to nobody) and *res communis* (belonging to everybody), the high seas have lately been generating an extraordinary amount of possessiveness. World powers periodically set aside large areas in which to detonate big bombs or test rockets. Fishermen of one country advise their neighbors to stop fishing "their" fish. Nations occasionally expand by annexing the adjacent seas. (A U.S. Naval officer recently showed the flag 35,-800 feet below the surface in the Marianas Trench.)

Ocean technology, its capabilites and its promise of enormous wealth, inspires much of this recent possessiveness. The "It's my ocean" attitude bears startling resemblance to rhetoric heard in another battle over ocean values—a battle out of which emerged the present concept of the high seas. This historic struggle not only set the stage for today's militant attitudes but suggests their possible outcome.

In the first part of the sixteenth century the concept of the high seas as *res communis* was virtually nonexistent. Genoa claimed the Ligurian Sea and Venice, the Adriatic. The Baltic was divided up by Sweden, Poland, and Denmark. Ships sailing north of Bergen required a royal license from Norway, which belonged to the Danish Crown. England regarded the North Sea as the "British Seas." Spain and Portugal resolved to split much of the Atlantic and Pacific between them, and in the Bulls of 1493 the Papacy approved of this monumental division.

These claims were not merely the fruit of the illusions of grandeur. Pirates, particularly out of the Barbary Coast, were marauding. Coastal nations felt it was only fair to share the costs of suppressing raiders with the users of the coastal seas. In keeping with their larger claim, Spain and Portugal advanced additional reasons for possession, mainly the rights obtained by discovery and exploration.

From a national standpoint the Iberian claim was a farsighted piece of statesmanship that recognized the capability of maritime technology to monopolize the trade, resources, and military advantages of the New World and the oceans between. In the control of the oceans lay Iberian control of the world, and Spain's fast galleons—sporting ample sail—carried wealth to outfit armies, artists, courtesans, and proseletyzing monks.

As other nations improved their shipping, they realized just how farsighted the Iberian claims were and also how fiercely defended. When John Hawkins carried African slaves to Spanish America, his prospective customers raided his ships in the Caribbean. Though thousands of miles from Spain, Hawkins was still in Spanish waters.

The nations that accepted or bowed to the Bulls of 1493 were, by the middle of the sixteenth century, thoroughly disenchanted. Because their ships, now using sail with greater facility than the galleons, were prevented from trading, another occupation beckoned. The piracy so assiduously practiced by the Saracens became national policy for England, the Netherlands, and France. Privateering was conducted under a meticulous cloak of legality. Queen Elizabeth would hand out letters of reprisal that authorized Hawkins and his protégé, Francis Drake, to raid Spanish ships (and thus furnish salvage for treasure hunters off Florida). Admiralty Courts judged captured galleons—"prizes"—as good or bad. Few prizes were declared bad, and the booty was divided between the Queen, the privateers, and the stockholders in the privateering vessels.

When Francis Drake collected a number of prizes while circumnavigating the globe, Philip II of Spain informed the Queen that her English seadog had no business being in his waters, much less freebooting there. Ignoring Philip's protest, the Queen knighted Drake and hung his navigation charts in her chambers. She then elevated the cause of privateering from national policy to a universal ideal: "The use of the air and sea is common to all; neither can any title to the ocean belong to any people or private man, forasmuch as neither nature nor regard of the public use permitteth any possession thereof." In one sentence the Queen managed to sum up the natural, political, and social character of the oceans. But her insight was quickly challenged.

The Spanish responded by launching the Armada. The lumbering *galleass*, half-oared, half-sailed, relied on ramming and boarding enemy squadrons. England's full-sailed, more maneuverable fleet under Drake avoided contact and depended on cannonading. They also shot "fyreworks" into Spanish sails. The English victory heralded the arrival of a truly national navy—a navy that could not only defend its country from invasion but could set the frontlines at the very shores of the enemy, however large his forces.

The defeat of the Armada did not serve to ratify the Queen's concept of a common sea. It only created a power struggle for sea supremacy. Spain and Portugal were far from ready to back down on their exclusive claims, and the enterprising Dutch were learning to trade, fish, and fight in a remarkable array of seagoing vessels. They cultivated a monopoly in spice and pepper and even began cornering the entire ocean hauling trade. They spawned a herring fishery that lived part of the year off the Scottish coast and inspired Scots to voice the same demands that Russian trawlers inspire in New Englanders today.

In Great Britain subsequent rulers regressed from the Queen's enlightened view of a common sea. Sovereignty was reaffirmed over the North Sea and taxes imposed on the Dutch herring fleet to refinance the country's uncompetitive fishery. The English also attempted to remedy another national shortcoming—a lack of sailors to man the Royal fleet. British captains periodically boarded merchant ships to draft British subjects and alleged deserters. The captain was sole judge as to who qualified as a British subject, and speaking the English language was sometimes dropped as a prerequisite. The British boldly required all ships in the British Seas to "vail bonnet" (strike the flag) in the presence of English ships, even of royal yachts. Ships that failed to salute received a shot through the mainsail and then had to reimburse the British government for the price of the shot.

Amidst all these projections of national sovereignty, privateering was still considered "patriotic retaliation." The resulting anarchy troubled many people. Some even held that privateering was morally wrong, regardless of its patriotic purpose. This disturbance came to a head in the Netherlands in 1603. The Dutch were still trying to horn in on the Portuguese monopoly of the East Indies trade, and the Portuguese had ambushed some Dutch ships and murdered their crews. Admiral Jacob

Heemskreck then privateered the carrack *Catherine*, bound for Lisbon, in the Straits of Malacca. A Dutch Admiralty Court adjudged the *Catherine* a good prize and distributed the proceeds to shareholders of the budding East India Company. Some shareholders, including Mennonites, refused their shares on the grounds that privateering was immoral and threatened to form a new trading company under French auspices. With its oceanic ambitions thus jeopardized, the Dutch government called on the state historiographer to justify privateering.

The historiographer happened to be Hugo Grotius, an engaging young man of twenty-one years. At eight Grotius had bought candles with Sunday money and penned Latin verses. At eleven he was graduated from the University of Leyden. At fourteen he was drafting treatises on astronomy and navigation and at fifteen, earning a Doctor of Laws at the University of Orleans. Grotius was a genius, incapable of producing an ordinary patriotic tract. Instead of defending privateering, Grotius set about to demolish the concept of exclusive use of the oceans. Queen Elizabeth's open-seas policy was to undergo a process of scholarly review, refinement, and amplification and come out as law. Began Grotius:

> The subject of our discussion is the Ocean, which was described in olden times as immense, infinite, the father of created things, and bounded only by the heavens; the Ocean, whose never-failing waters feed not only upon the springs and rivers and seas, according to the ancient belief, but upon the clouds, also, and in certain measure upon the stars themselves; in fine, that Ocean which encompasses the terrestrial home of mankind with the ebb and flow of its tides, and which cannot be held nor enclosed, being itself the possessor rather than the possessed.

To buttress this last phrase, Grotius marshaled authoritative testimony. He quoted Cicero: "What is so common . . . as is the sea to those who be tossed by the waves, or the shore to castaways." He cited Plautus: "The sea's most certainly common to all." He noted Seneca's similar sentiment (but omitted the tag line "it were a great part of human peace, if the seas were closed"). Plutarch, Socrates, Pericles, and the Bible were also called to testify. (Queen Elizabeth was not.) But for his chief witness Grotius called on an intellectual from the ranks of the very nation he was trying. He quoted the writings of a Spanish jurist, Vasquez: "In cases involving the sea or other waters, men do not and cannot possess any right other than that which relates to common use . . . since navigation cannot prove injurious save perhaps to the navigator himself, it is fitting that the power and right to impede this certainly should be denied to all persons. . . ." Grotius also cited Vasquez's comment on his country's presumptuous oceanic claim: an "absurdity."

After invoking natural, historical, and intellectual precedents for an ocean that cannot be "possessed," Grotius proceeded to lay down his own corollaries. On fishing: "The right of fishing ought everywhere to be exempt from tolls, least a servitude be imposed upon the sea, which is not susceptible of a servitude." On trade: "Anyone who abolishes this system of exchange, abolishes also the highly prized fellowship in which humanity is united."

Grotius then mocked the Portuguese for molesting ships that followed the natural law. "Are you indignant because we are acquiring a share in the winds and the sea? Pray, who hath promised you that you would always have these advantages?" Admiral Heemskreck was not only defending the East India Company. "The Dutch sailor knows that he is fighting in defense of the law of nations while his foes are fighting against the fellowship of mankind." Grotius entitled his brief *Mare Liberum*.

In place of exclusive claims and piratical retaliation, Grotius was offering the world a sea governed by a sense of mutual respect. Although his treatise was reprinted in several languages, it fell far short of immediate acceptance in a world in which kings were regarded as a law unto themselves and Machiavelli as their tutor. Grotius, as well as his *Mare Liberum,* was in fact rejected by his own people. He was swept up in a religious and political conflict peculir to the times, imprisoned, and smuggled out of Holland in a trunk. While serving as an adviser to Cardinal Richelieu he expanded his concept of the laws of nations and laid the groundwork for diplomatic protocol, rights of prisoners of war, international law, and other policies relevant to a world community.

While its chief intellect prospered in exile, the Netherlands quashed the pacifist spirit in the East India Company. After shouldering aside the Portuguese, the Dutch established their own monopoly in the Indies and rebuffed British traders "for seeking a harvest at our expense, they escaping the cost."

Great Britain took even more direct steps to refute Grotius' teachings. The Dutchman's remark that "fishing ought everywhere to be exempt from tolls" especially rankled the Tudors. John Selden, celebrated in poetry by Ben Jonson, admired by Milton, and a benefactor of Hobbes, was commissioned to refute *Mare Liberum.* In his *Mare Clausum* the scholarly Selden observed, "There are a few, who following chiefly some of the ancient Caesarian lawyers, endeavor to affirm, or beyond reason too easily admit, that all seas are common to the universality of mankind." One person particularly given to such reasoning was "a man of great learning and extraordinary knowledge in things both Divine and Humane; whose name is very frequent in the mouths of men everywhere." Selden then invoked his own authorities for a sea admitting of possession. He even cited King Canute's order to the tides not to touch the royal hem. Selden propounded his own law of the nations: "First, that the sea, by the law of nature or nations, is not common to all men, but capable of private dominion or property as well as the land; second, that the King of Britain is Lord of the Sea flowing about, as an inseparable and perpetual appendant of the British Empire."

During the seventeenth century the British and the Dutch engaged in hot and cold wars over Striking the

Flag and an attempt to rejuvenate the British fishery through the pockets of Dutch fishermen. Patriotic piracy continually seared the rising merchant order. In the midst of ocean anarchy Grotius' concepts, offering the prospect of armistice, became increasingly attractive. They also made possible a different type of possession. A sea common to all would reward most fully those nations who could best employ its resources, whether for fishing, trade, or military advantage. The Dutch, as the Portuguese before them, made up for their limited resources by pursuing just such a strategy. The British began paying less attention to sea salutes and impressment and more attention to improving the merchant marine, the high-seas fishing fleet, and conditions in the Royal Navy. A Scottish surgeon, Dr. James Lind, founder of nautical medicine, cured one impediment to Naval recruitment—the scurvy—with lemon juice. Shipbuilders saved His Majesty's fleet from another disabler, the tiny marine borer, by sheathing hulls in copper. Captain Cook surveyed the resources of the Pacific, and, in the next century, Darwin became acquainted with kelp aboard HMS *Beagle*. The British were oceanographers as well as mariners.

In the eighteenth and nineteenth centuries this national effort came to fruition. The Royal Navy bound an empire together. "The ships of English swarm like flies, their printed calicoes cover the whole earth and by the side of their swords the blades of Damascus are blades of grass," cried out a furious pasha. Their merchant and fishing fleets emerged dominant in maritime trade. In support of these global efforts, the British Foreign Office popularized *mare liberum*.

The rest of the world was, by this time, quite willing to accept a common ocean. Although Britain enjoyed dominance, other nations might still pursue their own maritime aspirations. The Ligurian, the Adriatic, the Baltic, the North, the Atlantic, and the Pacific emerged from servitude, free of both tolls and privateering. Grotius' law of the sea was most persuasive. It did not have to be ratified by a constitutional convention and encouraged reciprocity rather than retaliation. The self-regulating machinery of the shared-use concept—plenty of room for trading vessels and fishermen—could be set in motion. The Golden Rule at last became practicable.

One form of sea sovereignty did survive, however. Developing nations, sensitive about their independence, felt the need to secure their coastal waters from smuggling, impressment, neutrality violations, and other possible projections of sea power. Grotius himself admitted such a qualification. The question was, how wide was the territorial sea? Suggestions varied from twenty miles, or as far as the eye could see, to the range of coastal cannon, approximately three miles. One young nation, only then liberated from British control but not British sea dominance, decided to establish a specific boundary. In 1793 Thomas Jefferson, Secretary of State for the United States, chose the more modest cannonball standard.

The law of the sea does not rise alone from a national claim but from the acknowledgment of this claim by other nations. Less powerful nations responded favorably. Even England decided to establish a three-mile limit around her island. A narrow—but not necessarily three-mile—territorial sea became adopted in practice as part of maritime law. (Thomas Fulton, in his book, *Sovereignty of the Seas*, noted that Jefferson later devised another territorial sea. In 1807 he told France's Genet that our national jurisdiction extended "to the Gulf Stream, which was a natural boundary." His 1793 boundary proved to be longer lasting.)

In the same gradual and peaceful manner, as shipping increased, merchant navies began to draw up "rules of the road." So-called "contiguous zones" became recognized in customs, national security, and other specifically defined areas of national interest. At the same time, nations refrained from asserting past claims of sovereignty. In 1918, in responding to a letter from a citizen who said he had discovered oil forty miles out in the

Gulf of Mexico, the U.S. State Department said, "The United States has no jurisdiction over the ocean bottom of the Gulf of Mexico beyond the territorial waters adjacent to the coast."

In a world continually torn by doubts of the conviviality of the family of nations, the freedom of the high seas has emerged as one reassuring symbol. Every nation realizes in some way the yield of the sea, whether it be cloth carried by ship or canned salmon delivered to a supermarket. This yield is based on no sufferance of a reigning sea monarch. The common-sea concept, originated by Queen Elizabeth and refined by Grotius, now wins the praise of contemporary law scholars. In *The Public Order of the Oceans*, Professors Myres McDougal and William Burke observe, "The outcomes of inclusive, cooperative enjoyment—as several centuries have demonstrated—can be genuinely integrative, with all winning and none losing, in a tremendous production and wide sharing of benefits."

The success of this policy paved the way for the recent international treaties on Antarctica and outer space. What latent powers of international accord it will next uncover cannot be predicted; the search need not, however, lack for confidence and precedent.

Yet in 1945 the same country that abstained from jurisdiction over the Gulf of Mexico felt compelled to make two exclusive claims on the common sea. President Truman declared (1) that the seabed of the adjacent continental shelf belonged to the United States and (2) that the United States could establish fish conservation zones on the high seas. The first claim recognized that technology could transform the Gulf of Mexico and other offshore areas into a rich oil field. The second acknowledged that technology could deplete fish stocks, particularly in the case of salmon, and reduce one nation's conservation efforts to a mockery. The United States made these declarations after consulting with other nations and inviting them to do the same. However circumspectly stated, these claims could not help but foster

what has followed. All the old issues—sharing of resources, methods (and motives) of conservation, limits
of the territorial sea, occupation of the sea, and requirements of national security—have flared anew under the
pressure of technological advances far mightier than full
sail and "fyreworks." These advances have made the
ocean a resource of far greater dimensions than a highway for navigation, and long-time allies find themselves
disagreeing over what it means for the law of the sea.
Just how ironic and bitter these disagreements can be
has been dramatized in a relatively unfamiliar ocean
area.

16.

The Case of the
Flag-Flying Fish

EXTENDING two thousand miles out from the western coast of Central and South America is a generous stretch of ocean called the Eastern Tropical Pacific. Unlike the Mediterranean, it cannot claim to be the basin of western civilization. Coastal nations are relatively young and are developing with eyes traditionally looking inward. Unlike the nearby Caribbean, the Eastern Tropical Pacific offers few exotic honeymoon settings. Its islands are small, infrequent, and bizarre—strange archipelagos such as the reptilian Galapagos, where Darwin rode tortoises and confirmed his theory of evolution.

Yet the Eastern Tropical Pacific has its own virtues. It is as beautiful as any ocean can possibly be. In sailing patois, "The air is so clear you can see three days ahead." Winds and cat's paw breezes forever stir, ruffling the blue waters. By night the clear air reveals a sky more snowy than dark, flooded with the cold-white stars.

Soaring winds ("strong enough to unhair a dog") can lash the waters into leaping waves, as dark clouds,

193

gashed by lightning, form overhead. The Eastern Tropical Pacific is suddenly blacked out by a *chubasco*, a tropical hurricane.

Other seas and other oceans can lay claim to balmy weather and blue vistas, but one quality sets the Eastern Tropical Pacific apart. The tantalizingly opaque waters of other oceans rarely reveal the life within to casual observers. A flock of seabirds, a porpoise fin, or a whale blow can be a welcome diversion aboard an ocean liner. But the Eastern Tropical Pacific is not at all reticent about its inner life. Flocks of seabirds are as common as clouds. There are whale blows aplenty, seals bark, and dinoflagellate blooms tint the sea by day and at night ignite in phosphorescence. A porpoise does not merely show his fin, he can vault clear of the ocean, all the time revolving in the air. The spinner porpoise can do this in perfect accord with a thousand of his own kind, and the ocean suddenly resembles a stadium in which athletes are performing a thousand simultaneous somersaults. This ocean is the *alive* ocean, flaunting its fertility like the green parrot jungles of Central America.

A key to this fertility lies in the constant winds that move the ocean in great, criss-crossing currents; the Humboldt, the North equatorial current, the South equatorial current, the South equatorial countercurrent and the California current. Upwelling thrives amid this perpetual motion by replacing a depleted surface with cool, nutrient-rich waters from thousand-foot depths. (The nearness of the Equator is deceptive when one plunges a hand in this coolness.) The recharged waters sustain pastures of plankton, which, in turn, nourish swimming crabs, anchovy, anchovetas, sardines, and other small fish and crustacea. Sharks, sailfish, bonito, and mackerel all stalk the tiny predators of plankton. One hunter moves in schools as thick as buffalo herds, as swift as squadrons of waterfowl. Once spied by a school of sleek yellowfin tuna, the small fish may rush to the surface in a frantic attempt to escape their environment, only to be spied by seabirds that drop like white

darts. Amid the splashing frenzy the Eastern Tropical
Pacific once more celebrates its fertility. It is this fertility
that attracts high-seas fishing fleets and triggers one
of the fiercest, most relentless battles for supremacy in
man's predatory history.

The object of this competition, the yellowfin tuna,
ranks in the aristocracy of fishdom. Most coastal fish are
dun-colored, to blend with the sea floor. The yellowfin
sports the beautiful camouflage of the high seas, a metal-
lic blue top and a silvery underside, all fine-scaled. The
blue foils detection from above, the silver from below,
and the fins and a stripe along the body give off a yellow
glow that suggests that a tuna may semaphore by flashing his body.

Yellowfins can spawn at all times of the year. The eggs
hatch in forty-eight hours, and within a year the larvae
can grow into seven-pound fish. Tuna larvae are prized
by small fish and adult tuna. Their mortality rate, according to biologist Witold Klawe of the Inter-American
Tropical Tuna Commission, runs close to one hundred
per cent. To compensate for this astronomic mortality a
tuna can spawn up to eight million eggs at one time. An
egg that manages to survive will weigh one hundred
forty-nine pounds by its fourth birthday.

To evade sharks and to sustain its swift growth, the
yellowfin requires exceptional speed, range, and depth-
sounding capabilities. It can range a thousand miles and
more, sound more than eighty fathoms, and attain a
speed of forty miles an hour. (The fastest clocked marine animal is a tuna.) Its fins symbolize this mobility.
Coastal fish wear stubby and webbed fins, closely re-
sembling a whisk broom. Those of the yellowfin are long
and lean. Its pectorals span out like wings to brake or
stabilize underwater flight. The tail fin is an arc—a
sweeping scimitar. Setting this simple screw in motion is
a deep-bodied torso of concentric muscle. The flesh is
not white but pinkish, colored by tremendous amounts
of oxygen-giving blood that powers high-seas foraging.
(The temperature of most fish equals that of the water;
the spirited tuna is generally ten degrees centigrade

warmer than his environment.) The yellowfin forages after squid, flying fish, swimming crabs, octopus, and the general abundance of the Eastern Tropical Pacific. After examining the stomachs of four thousand yellowfins, marine biologist Franklin Alverson (presently with the Van Camp Seafood Company) classified their diet as "rather cosmopolitan." Alverson even found wood, kelp, feathers, and "unidentified material" in these indulgent somachs.

A great fishery requires an abundant stock, and the rapid growth and turnover of the yellowfin meets this requirement. The fish must also be nutritious and appealing. The protein content of tuna matches that of red meat without the accompanying fat calories. It contains iodine to prevent goiter, fluorine to thwart tooth decay, phosphorous to build bone, and vitamin B_{12} to enrich red blood cells. The yellowfin perfectly exemplifies the nutritious richness of the ocean, a richness many food authorities see as the key to man's survival on a congested planet.

Theoretically, this valuable resource, like other fish of the high seas, is common property, available to all individuals and all nations in need of its value. Yet this universal availability is restricted by another factor, the ability to catch and distribute the fish.

In the age of the Incas couriers ran one-mile laps to deliver tuna to the Inca capital of Cuzco, one hundred thirty miles inland. Their balsa rafts, however, effectively limited their ability to pursue this great fish. "Xatunkama" remained a delicacy for emperors. The wooden craft of successor nations were little better. Even though tuna swam within three miles of the shore, protein malnutrition became a fact of life for many Latin Americans.

Early in this century Zane Grey, a writer of westerns, reported four-hour struggles with an unusually spirited sport fish off Central America. David Starr Jordan, a famous biologist at Stanford University, identified the fish as a yellowfin, then considered a scarce species. The skipjack, a smaller tuna, was spotted in the same waters. Such reports came to the eager attention of fishermen in San Diego and the Los Angeles harbor town of San Pedro. These fishermen have a great tradition. Their Italian, Portuguese, and Slavic ancestors trapped tuna in the Mediterranean and harpooned whales in the Atlantic. They immigrated to California to pursue bowhead and gray whales in the Pacific and open up the California sardine industry which John Steinbeck dramatized in *Cannery Row*, but the California current, rich as it is in fishes, could not contain their ambitions. Hake, saury, anchovy, mackerel, and other abundant stocks are nutritious but not particularly marketable. The main tuna species, albacore, is sporadic. The fishermen had access to a great market, America. All they needed was a fish. The yellowfin and skipjack beckoned, even though they lay in another clime and challenged the most skilled fisherman.

The Cabrals, the Misetichs, the Felandos, and others began switching allegiance from their modest coastal fishing boats to the tuna "clipper," high-bowed, dieselpowered, and often mortgaged to the fantail. Brine refrigeration was installed to prevent the catch from deteriorating on three- or four-month voyages. Housed in a small ship's closet to keep the homeless fishermen company was a miniature altar crowned with an alabaster Mary.

The clippers sprouted a tall lookout mast, reminiscent of the New England whalers. Since tuna do not blow, the "mast man" had to find other signs in the blue world of the Tropical Pacific. A porpoise school is always investigated, for tuna often cruise beneath them. At night a dinoflagellate bloom can coat cruising tuna in phosphorescence and alert the clipper. In rising to the surface after small fish, the splashing tuna attract sharks and seabirds. Feeding seabirds become seeing-eye dogs, leading the blind clippers to fleeting encounters with their well-concealed quarry.

Tuna schools turn, dive, and ascend all together. These tightly disciplined schools even sort themselves out according to size—a potentially perfect set-up for a single toss of the net. Unfortunately, there were few nets big enough to corral yellowfin, much less men agile enough to set and retrieve a giant net before sharks devoured the imprisoned catch. The proud California fishermen in their streamlined clippers were forced to rely on a grueling, primitive method of fishing. Once the seabirds had led the clipper to a tuna "boil," a crew member would "chum" (toss out live anchovetas or other bait fish scooped inshore and kept in bait wells). Other crew members unhinged ramps on the side of the clipper. They stepped down onto these ramps, their legs awash in the Pacific, their hands gripping bamboo poles that dangled a barbless hook shrouded in chicken feathers. The feather lures were flicked into the boil. The frenzied tuna failed to discriminate between the lures and the anchovetas. Once he felt a wrench, the fisherman, like a human crane, would arc a forty-pound tuna overhead. At the top of the arc, the fisherman would release the barbless hook by simply letting up on the tension. The world's fastest fish plopped onto the clipper deck as the released hook was whipped back into the tuna boil. This feat was accomplished in one sweeping motion and repeated for hours on end by a dozen men knee-deep in the Pacific. In schools of large-size tuna, as many as five fishermen would link their poles to a common lure, hook a tropical tuna, pull together, and arc an iridescent, hundred-pound torso over their backs to the clipper deck. The tuna, their mouths bleeding, their iridescence fading to gray, drummed on the deck with their tail fins—now just cargo in the brine tanks, awaiting a quick-freeze.

Sometimes a human cry would rise above the grunts of labor and the beat of tail fins. One tired fisherman had carelessly flicked his line and, like a zipper, the hook opened up a co-worker's back. Sometimes a man would slip and fall into the Pacific. Usually he could clamber back before another eager participant in the tuna boil— a hungry shark—could claim him.

Pole fishing, primitive, dangerous, but stunningly ex-

ecuted, began overcoming the challenge of the yellowfin. Meanwhile, California fishermen who stuck with the
sardine discovered that their efficient purse seine nets
had effectively depleted the sardine stocks. Cannery
Row became a ghost town, lately revived as a tourist
attraction.

While the tuna fleet evolved the technology of tuna
capture, California canners perfected the technology of
preparation and packaging, enabling them to steam,
bone, gut, and slice the yellowfin, wrap it in sanitary
steel, and make its bone-building, tooth-preserving,
weight-reducing values available to a nation of meat
eaters. This last factor proved something of a problem,
but the brine-frozen corpses that went into the cannery
emerged as delectable Chicken of the Sea, Breast of
Chicken, and Starkist. On television, buxom mermaids
(wearing modest bras) and animated tuna would extoll
the nutritious products of the Eastern Tropical Pacific.

America's dietary appropriation of the Alive Ocean
was abetted by events occurring in North Pacific waters.
Here Pacific salmon, America's chief canned fish, was
proving far less challenging than the yellowfin. The
purse seines, gill nets, fish traps, and river nets of Japanese, Canadian, and American fishermen were severely
taxing salmon stocks. With salmon prices rising, the pursuit of the tropical tuna so intensified that by the early
1950's the pace set by pole fishing was found wanting.
Across the Pacific other high-seas fishermen were exploiting tuna stocks with an absurdly simple but highly
successful strategy. Instead of pursuing feeding seabirds,
the Japanese tuna fleet merely drops stationary lines into
the ocean. These lines, which can be set at any depth,
are attached to the beautiful purple glass globes that
occasionally wash up on California beaches. The lines
contain hundreds of hooks baited with frozen saury. The
success of "long lining" depends on the extent of coverage, and extensive coverage, in turn, depends on a ready
supply of inexpensive labor. The Japanese began string-
ing the Western Pacific with long lines. In one day a

Japanese vessel could set and retrieve sixty-five miles of long line containing twenty-five hundred hooks. Tuna that pounced on saury found themselves dangling in midocean with a hook for a noose. The victim next door might be a shark or a marlin.

The tuna at the end of Japanese long lines began flowing into California canneries. American tuna fishermen were soon selling yellowfin at prices that did not always meet expenses, much less mortgage payments. The prolonged search for feeding seabirds, the back-breaking, hand-blistering job of pole fishing, and the task of riding out *chubascos* only put some boat owners deeper and deeper into the red.

To stay in the tuna competition, the American tuna fleet felt compelled to ask for tariff protection against Japanese imports. The Eastern Tropical Pacific had its first brush with the ironic politics of high-seas fishing. The American fleet felt it had a good case. It had pioneered America's only true high-seas fishing fleet since the New England whaling days. In World War II the Navy drafted the tuna clippers (along with their crews) to help supply isolated Pacific island outposts.

But these accomplishments seemed to run contrary to current American policy. Since World War II the United States had made improvement of foreign fisheries an object of foreign aid. A major fishing nation before the war, the Japanese eagerly accepted such aid, and tuna fishing helped facilitate its economic recovery. The United States was not inclined to jeopardize this recovery with tariffs. The Japanese already abstain from fishing Pacific salmon in certain high-seas areas out of respect for Canadian and American conservation efforts. The American tuna fisherman could survive only by fishing the Eastern Tropical Pacific harder and harder with more efficient methods and hope that the abundance of the tropical tuna could hold.

In 1956 the clipper *Anthony M.* set out after tuna, but when the mast man cried "boil" no bait was chummed, no ramps unhinged, and no poles, grabbed. On reaching the boil, the clipper, proceeding at full speed, launched a power skiff off the stern. The two-man skiff and the clipper sped off in opposite directions and then started closing toward one another in a giant circle. When they met, a fat mound of nylon netting was spooled into the ocean to form a wall of webbing some two hundred feet deep and more than a half mile in diameter. The only exit for tuna lay downward, but a winch on the clipper swiftly drew this exit shut like a purse string. A power boom contracted the massive circle into a bag. Power-driven dip nets brailed the thrashing tuna into brine tanks, as crew members strove mightily to disentangle stray porpoises.

Purse seining had finally caught up with the tropical tuna. Although five pole fishermen were required to land one hundred-pound yellowfin, the Puretic power block atop the boom could reel in one hundred tons of netted tuna. The whine of gears replaced the grunts of labor. Conversion to purse seining costs over more than one hundred thousand dollars per clipper, but the tuna fleet had little choice. By 1960 many clippers were converting in order to meet the competition from the Western Pacific. That same year the Alive Ocean yielded a record two hundred thirty-four million pounds of yellowfin. The tuna fleet was back in competition.

Meanwhile the Japanese were running out of tuna in the Western Pacific. The Indian Ocean proved rich in tuna stocks, but, again, long lining soon thinned them out. Tuna cruised in the Atlantic, but apparently not in great numbers. Accordingly, Japanese long-lining vessels began appearing on the periphery of the Eastern Tropical Pacific. Soon they were dropping fifty million hooks a year—hooks that dangled marlin, sailfish, big-eye tuna, and the prized yellowfin. The competition was becoming more intense—Canadian fishermen made their debut—but the Eastern Tropical Pacific was still prepared to fill more nets, more brine tanks, and more mouths.

Nations whose eyes looked traditionally inward began

responding. In 1950 plant machinery designed to process a species of anchovy (*anchoveta peruana*) in Peru into fishmeal for poultry feed was secretly installed in a secluded Peruvian bay. California's declining sardine industry created a ready opportunity. The secrecy was necessary to avoid arousing the opposition of a powerful fertilizer industry. Peru's guano industry is based on island seabird droppings, and the profuse droppings are based on a seabird diet of anchovy. Before the guano industry could promote defensive fish restrictions, the Eastern Tropical Pacific reaffirmed its astounding fertility. Within a decade Peru was landing more fish tonnage than any other nation, thanks to the six-inch anchovy. Some fifty shipyards now outfit anchoveta fishermen. Peruvian Indians, brought down from the Andes, corral anchoveta schools with walls of webbing. Fishmeal plants are so numerous in the port of Callao that they contaminate the air, and even though the plants pulp fourteen million tons of anchoveta yearly, enough remain to enable the seabirds to deposit guano six inches thick on rocky, offshore islands.

The anchoveta fishery is an unsophisticated affair, but the coastal nations are intent on competing for still bigger prizes. Mexico, Costa Rica, Colombia, Ecuador, Peru, and Chile send out bait boats and *bolicheros* (small purse seiners without freezers) after tuna, but these Latin American countries also compete on another level.

When President Truman annexed the seabed of the adjacent continental shelf, Chile, Ecuador and Peru looked at theirs. Although some nations enjoy shelves that extend out over more than two hundred miles, the "CEP" nations (as they are called in legal and diplomatic circles) found their shelf to be as narrow as five miles. The prime benefit of this shelf—which permits open sea resources like the yellowfin to come inshore—could be exploited by all nations. The three countries refused to be short-changed by geography. Citing the Truman Proclamation as a precedent, they extended their borders to "possess sole sovereignty and jurisdiction . . . not less than 200 miles" from the coast. Sovereignty embraced the resources of the seabed and the sea above. As P. E. Corbett, a scholar in international law, observed, "The pupils had bettered their instruction." (Some Central American nations have since made similar claims.) The fish of the Eastern Tropical Pacific were suddenly wearing national flags.

As further precedent for their claim, the CEP nations expanded considerably on the spirit of the Truman proclamation on fishery conservation by declaring in a joint pronouncement, "The human population of the coast forms part of the biological chain which originates in the adjoining sea and which extends from the microscopic vegetable and animal life to the higher mammals, among which we count man. These 'bioma' are proper to each region . . . and it is, therefore, a prime duty of every coastal state to insure that they are not destroyed in the only way that this is possible, which is by the depradation of man." A permanent agency, the Conference on the Use and Conservation of the Marine Resources of the South Pacific, was then formed.

On the "bioma" basis, the CEP claim is overly modest. The ocean-wide range of tuna and whales would require similar expansive sovereignty. In reality, the nations which lacked the technology to compete effectively in the Eastern Tropical Pacific also lacked the scientific capability to understand, much less manage, its migrant resources. The CEP nations had not spent millions of dollars in fishery conservation, as America and Canada had in the case of the Pacific salmon. No fish in the Eastern Tropical Pacific required such lavish care. This ocean was not overfished. If anything, it was underfished. The CEP nations had not even consulted with foreign fishermen before proclaiming their exclusive conservation zone, as America and Canada had done with Japan in regard to salmon in the North Pacific Fisheries Convention.

As others have done before, the CEP nations invoked

conservation to serve a less selfless purpose. The tuna clippers with their jaunty lookout masts, the huge seine nets hanging from the power boom like magnificent filigree, the brine tanks stuffed with yellowfin hard as logs, all these offshore sights were galling reminders of "economic inequality of states," as one Latin American diplomat explained. That these clippers could pluck yellowfin within three miles of their shore and transport the catch five thousand miles away constituted injustice in the eyes of the CEP nations. To them the freedom of the high-seas concept was not one to be cherished but to be wary of, a potential lever to widen even further the gap between the haves and have-nots, a means by which America might usurp the resources of the adjacent ocean.

Laying claim to exclusive possession of an ocean area is useless without the means to enforce and exploit such a claim. On this point the CEP nations revealed an acquaintance with Tudor tactics. There was no intent to prohibit fishing, just to capitalize on it.

Permits would be required to fish in the newly acquired waters. Foreign fishermen who failed to purchase permits would be seized, their boats impounded, and their violation heard before a special court. The court could assess fines one to five times the value of the catch aboard the boat. Proceeds from the fines would be divided evenly among the three countries, to be used to improve fishing technology.

In 1954 destroyers in the Peruvian Navy spotted a whaling fleet one hundred miles offshore. The fleet hastily departed. After bombing and strafing attacks and a pursuit that ended three hundred miles offshore, five whaling vessels were escorted into a Peruvian port. The ships, flying the flag of Panama and manned mainly by Germans, were owned by Aristotle Onassis, then a resident of France and a citizen of Argentina. When asked for the ship's log, Captain Wilhelm Reichert said he had thrown it overboard in the belief that Panama and Peru were at war. A Peruvian court, deeming this response an "ingenious excuse," noted that the fleet had taken three thousand whales, levied a three million dollar fine, and gave the fleet owner five days to pay. Mr. Onassis protested. So did Panama. Even the United Kingdom protested, since Lloyd's of London carried ninety per cent of the fleet's insurance. The United States protested. American insurance companies carried the remaining ten per cent. Mr. Onassis's country of citizenship did not protest, for Argentina claims an epicontinental shelf, which strongly resembles the CEP claim. The five ships were finally released . . . after the three million had been paid. The CEP nations were serious about putting flags on whales and tropical tuna.

Peru, Ecuador, Chile, Colombia, and even Panama began seizing tuna clippers, often from the deck of the very gunboats provided by the U.S. military assistance program. Tuna captains responded in a variety of ways. When the Ecuadorian Navy started to seize two clippers, twenty-one other clippers formed a circle around their threatened brethren, "something like the old covered wagon circle." The threat of gunfire broke up the circle, and the two captured clippers paid twelve thousand dollars in fines. Seventeen tuna vessels conducted an anchor-in in a Peruvian port to protest a similar fine. The anchor-in concluded after Peru collected thirty-one thousand dollars in fish permits.

The United States State Department contends with frustration, too. Chagrined that the Truman Proclamation was cited as a precedent for the CEP claim, the United States protested that expansive national "maritime zones" violate traditional freedom of navigation. The CEP nations slightly qualified their position: the claim to sovereignty extended only to resources, not to navigation rights. Unsatisfied, the United States helped foster two global conferences on the Law of the Sea at Geneva in 1958 and 1960. The little-known Eastern Tropical Pacific Ocean had become a principal factor in a review of the precepts of Queen Elizabeth and Grotius.

The eighty-eight assembled nations readily agreed to codify the traditional freedom of navigation. A Convention on Fishing recognized the right of coastal states to set conservation regulations in the adjacent ocean and the right of fishing nations to be consulted on these regulations. A procedure was set up to arbitrate fishery disputes. Unfortunately, the eighty-eight nations could not agree on a specific limit to coastal jurisdiction or on how regulated fish stocks are to be allocated among the fishing nations. The arbitration procedure has yet to be used.

Unable to rely on the results from the two global sea conferences, the perplexed State Department suggested submitting the dispute in the Alive Ocean to the International Court of Justice. The CEP nations declined. They follow the United States in refusing to submit to the compulsory jurisdiction of this court in international matters. When the United States suggested joint conservation efforts, the CEP nations tagged recognition of their claim to such harmony.

In the Congress, San Diego Congressman Robert "Tuna Bob" Wilson proposed cutting foreign assistance to countries who practice high-seas "shakedowns." The Peruvian Parliament, in turn, cried "political blackmail" and "economic aggression"; there was talk of appropriating Standard Oil holdings. Tuna Bob then suggested that the U.S. Navy "show the flag" to Latin gunboats. Other Congressmen picked up this virile tactic in examining State Department officials at committee hearings.

A nation that attempts to reset or "correct" the seaward claims of other nations however, can only harvest more mischief. Where does the Seventh Fleet show the flag? At three miles? The United States, Japan, and the European countries are the principal retainers of this territorial breadth. Six miles? This distance is precisely half the breadth that many nations, including Russia, observe. In 1966 the United States adopted a nine-mile exclusive fishery jurisdiction beyond its three-mile territorial sea. Interestingly enough, many clipper seizures have occurred within the range of this popular twelve-mile limit. Among more ambitious nations India claims a hundred-mile fishing zone, Argentina a two hundred-mile zone, and Korea a zone that varies from twenty to two hundred fifty miles wide.* If the American tuna fleet thinks it has troubles, it ought to try, like the Japanese, to fish off Korea.

Another factor weighs heavily in any response by the United States. To the peoples of Latin America the CEP claim becomes a symbolic defiance of American imperialism. A government that rolls back the two hundred-mile boundary under pressure from America could well be overthrown. Aggressive action by the United States thus risks playing directly into the hands of extremists. Such are the factors that make arbitration of the high-seas fishery one of diplomacy's most demanding challenges.

The United States Government resolved to adopt a rather humiliating stance for a world power. The tuna fleet, which as fleet spokesman Felando says, must "carry the burden of this country's policy of freedom of the seas," is required to pay fines without resistance. The United States will then reimburse these fines and, at the same time, maintain its non-recognition of the CEP claim. The U.S. Fishermen's Protective Act, as law scholar Henry Reiff observes, echoes the days when America paid ransom to Barbary pirates. In tapping the financial resources of this act, Ecuador leads with forty-three seizures as of late 1966, whereas Peru advances rapidly with twenty-five seizures.

As the fishery competition in the Eastern Tropical Pacific becomes an ever thornier political problem, it also generates a conservation problem—one whose swift solution is vital to the future of the ocean's potential. In 1961 it was revealed that what had happened to the sardine in California, the salmon in the Pacific Northwest, and the whales throughout the world was finally happening to the apparently endless yellowfin: depletion.

The Inter-American Tropical Tuna Commission made this ominous discovery. Unlike the Conference on the

* Appendix E lists national claims to coastal fishery jurisdiction.

Use and Conservation of the Marine Resources of the South Pacific, the IATTC enjoys the scientific capability to back up conservation claims. The Commission has its headquarters next door to the Scripps oceanographic complex in La Jolla. It also maintains branch offices in Peru, Puerto Rico, and San Pedro, California. A distinguished scientific staff, recruited internationally, has published more than eighty papers on the biodynamics of the Eastern Tropical Pacific.

The IATTC is, in the tradition of other regional fish commissions, set up to conduct research on fish stocks and recommend regulations for their conservation. Similar commissions focus on the Northeast Pacific Ocean, the Northwest Atlantic, the Northeast Atlantic, and are beginning to be established in the Southern Hemisphere. The IATTC differs from other commissions in that it was set up in 1949, when the resources of the Eastern Tropical Pacific appeared to defy depletion. This foresight was due in large part to the leadership of men like Dr. Wilbert Chapman, then fisheries special assistant to the Secretary of State and now Director of Resources for Van Camp Seafood Company. Schooled in the salmon and halibut conflicts of the North Pacific, Dr. Chapman learned that fishery conservation is useless without agreements that recognize the international nature of fish stocks. Mexico, Panama, and Canada now adhere to the Convention while Japan works closely with the Commission. (Writer's note—Canada has subsequently been admitted while Ecuador has dropped out.)

The Commission's first director, Dr. Milner Schaefer, was also experienced in the Pacific salmon conflicts. There he learned that fishery conservation can be useless without adequate scientific evidence of the full nature and extent of the environment of the fish. Salmon biologists once thought they had discerned a high-seas boundary line beyond which salmon from Canadian and American streams did not roam. The Japanese fishermen who agreed to observe this boundary nonetheless were delighted to discover that the salmon persisted in crossing it and entering Japanese nets.

As Dr. Schaefer recognized, such scientific errors can be quite costly in an ocean arena in which fishery conflicts escalate to the armed seizure stage, and Congressmen offhandedly suggest Showing the Flag. Yet he had to divine the tolerances of a fish with little of the scientific notoriety of the river-ascending salmon. One talisman did exist. Catch records dating back to 1934 showed how yellowfin stocks responded to various fishing intensities, from the slack-off during World War II, when the tuna fleet was mobilized and went to war, to the hectic period of postwar fishery. In 1957 Dr. Schaefer announced that the yellowfin's "maximum sustainable yield" (MSY) would be one hundred ninety-four million pounds annually. Above this catch figure, he concluded, fishermen would expend more effort to catch fewer and smaller yellowfin. No Commission biologist had ever indulged in such a prediction.

In 1960 the tuna fleet accomplished its record catch, some forty million pounds above Dr. Schaefer's MSY. In 1965 the fleet, better equipped than ever before, was able to land only one hundred eighty million pounds. The impact of the purse seine conversion had confirmed Dr. Schaefer's scientific audacity and fish technology's self-destructive nature.

When Dr. Schaefer left the Commission to direct the University of California's Institute of Marine Resources, he was replaced by Dr. John Kask, a Canadian biologist, who was immediately faced with the task of recommending conservation regulations to nine nations intent on competing, rather than cooperating, in matters concerning the Eastern Tropical Pacific.

Dr. Kask, another veteran of the fishery conflicts of the Pacific Northwest, realized that just as in the case of salmon, conservation regulations would be useless if they failed to encompass the full range of the yellowfin. Many tuna range ocean-wide and require ocean-wide regulations. IATTC scientists suspected that yellowfin tuna prefer a regional range. Tagging experiments and blood samples from yellowfin stocks in the Central Pacific confirmed that these stocks in the Eastern Pacific form a distinct population unit. A conservation zone was proposed whose shoreward boundary embraced twelve nations, from California to Chile.

Setting aside breeding areas as fish preserves is one popular conservation measure, but yellowfin spawning preferences remain unknown. The restriction of advanced fishing gear, such as power boats, is another possible measure, but the Commission did not want to penalize efficiency by regulating purse seiners.

The Commission finally recommended closure of yellowfin fishing after attainment of an annual quota. The established quota would ensure stock recuperation; enforcement would be up to the good faith of abiding nations. In 1961, a year after the record catch, the IATTC recommended such a quota.

It is galling to anyone to accept restrictions as a reward for improved performance, and fishermen are no exception. The tuna clipper captains in their handsome mortgaged clippers reverted to the "fish are so thick you can walk on them" stance. Fishermen are always willing to repose more faith in the mystique of an ever-bountiful nature than in the statistics of conservationists. Fish regulations conserve fish, not necessarily fishermen, but regional fish commissions only have to convince nations. Condoning unrestricted exploitation did not appeal to the United States, Japan, or the CEP nations. After four years of persuasion the nations agreed to establish a yearly quota.

The quota first went into effect in the fall of 1966 and, at that time, I went down to the tuna docks in San Diego. While tourists snapped photos, clipper crews were nostalgically mending their nets, like the widow who persists in mending her husband's Sunday suit. Some of the menders were far from philosophical. "How are you going to trust those guys down south?" responded one fisherman when I asked his opinion of the quota. Another griped, "If the government is going to regulate us, they should subsidize us like the farmers." The men who contend with *chubascos*, Peruvian gunboats, and Japanese long liners now face the prospect of making a year's living in eight or nine months. A quota system may only serve to intensify competition for a high-seas fishery by imposing a time limit.

The harried contestants once more finds themselves turning toward technology for salvation. The United States, through the Bureau of Commercial Fisheries, now seeks to upgrade the fishing fleet it has previously tended to ignore. A possible buoy system would telemeter oceanic data from the Eastern Tropical Pacific to mainland computers programmed to identify likely tuna locales. To advance tuna detection beyond primitive seabird sightings the Bureau is applying submarine sonar to tuna detection. ("It takes about the same kind of knowledge about the ocean to catch cheaply both tuna and submarines," Dr. Chapman has noted.) To expedite tuna capture the Bureau studies the possibility of herding the fish into nets by manipulating their schooling behavior. The Bureau also subsidizes new, million-dollar tuna clippers that search for virgin tuna grounds off the Atlantic seaboard, off Africa, and in the Central Pacific.

The Bureau wondered if chemical "shark repellents" would discourage sharks from attacking tuna caught in nets. Its scientists tossed chunks of tuna into a covey of thirty sharks, then hosed the water with an inky shark repellent. The sharks continued to sup blissfully with black repellent streaming through their gills. When one shark slid alongside the research vessel and snapped off the end of the hose emitting the repellent, the scientists called it quits. As a more workable alternative, the Bureau is now seeking to encourage a commercial shark fishery in South America. In Mexico an island penal colony processes sharks into hides and meat.

Backed up by increasing technical and financial resources, the tuna captain is becoming a practicing oceanographer, a corporate entity and an instrument, if not occasionally a victim, of national policy. The Eastern Tropical Pacific is spawning one of the world's more voracious fishing machines.

To keep abreast Japan is introducing tuna purse

seiners into its fleet. New competitors promise to emerge. Soviet oceanographers have been studying the Eastern Tropical Pacific and filming the new American tuna clippers in action. They are also training Cuba's expanding tuna fleet. (Two fish-factory ships, the *Arkovo* and the *Skryplev*, left the Soviet Far East in late 1966 to fish off Mexico for everything from sardines to bluefin tuna.)

The CEP countries are procuring purse seine clippers from European shipyards. Peru also has a contract with America's Portsmouth naval yards, but not for fishing vessels. Instead of surplus American gunboats, Peru wants the latest in patrol craft to man its expansive marine frontier.

This mobilization of fish and patrol technology makes actions once considered unlikely quite possible. If Peru seizes a million-dollar clipper subsidized by American taxpayers, the United States may feel compelled to cut foreign aid, institute boycotts, arrange armed tuna convoys, and push out its own seaward boundaries for good measure. The CEP nations may well strafe recalcitrant clippers, lease exclusive yellowfin rights to Russian purse seiners, expropriate Standard Oil, and withhold UN support of American policies. Amid such political carnage, the regional fish commission will disappear into oblivion and the hapless yellowfin will be hunted to utter depletion. Such prospects make the promise of fish technology and of oceans like the Eastern Tropical Pacific an ironic curse. This curse will haunt the toss of each fish net, the set of each long line, and the cast of each feather lure as long as the underlying issue of all modern fishery disputes—the allocation of resources in a sea supposedly common to all—remains unresolved.

17.

Fish Without Flags

In his day Grotius found a most felicitous solution to the problem of divvying up fish in a sea common to all—citing the existence of more fish than any one fisherman or nation could possibly handle. The giant purse seines of developed nations, the ambitions of developing nations, and a hungry world population of three billion make this solution no longer viable. If adherence to the common-sea concept means that all comers may harvest fish limited only by technical finesse, this concept is today irrelevant. If, however, adherence means a commitment by nations to share in both conservation and development of fisheries, a common sea holds enormous potential benefit. The United States and the CEP nations have been making a case for this very proposition while locked in their thorny stalemate.

The capability that fostered Peru's astounding anchovy industry came in large part from the United States; indeed, the Peruvian government recognized the contribution of fishery expert Brayton Wilbur with a medal. The first secret processing plants used machinery from the dying California sardine industry—machinery sold on very liberal terms. Mr. Manual Elguerra of

Peru's National Society of Fishes recently declared, "It would be unfair of me if I were to omit special recognition for the permanent friendly attitude and the advice and assistance given to the Peruvian fishing enterprise by American institutions and scientists, mainly from the State of California. Their technical contribution to the growth of one of Peru's main economic pillars is in line with the recognized generosity of the American Government and the American people toward their sister nations." Peru's ability to strike a critical balance between the fishmeal industry, the guano industry, and the anchovy stocks will depend in great part on this same technical source.

The benefit from such cooperation seems somewhat one-sided until one discovers that prime participants in the anchovy industry include Van Camp, Star Kist, B. F. Goodrich (synthetic fish floats) and other enterprising American interests.

When we transfer such scientific and economic cooperation to the entire Eastern Tropical Pacific, we come tantalizingly close to its potential to nourish a good part of the world. At present this ocean largely serves the needs of the United States, a country with a food surplus. (Our cats consume more yellowfin as pet food than do the people of Peru.) Even the bulk of harvested anchovies leaves the Southern Hemisphere as an export item. Anchovy fishmeal winds up in the crops of chickens who, in turn, wind up in the stomachs of people in North America and Europe. Yet the Alive Ocean contains enough untapped fish stocks to eliminate protein malnutrition in Latin America and still help North America keep its figure. Much of its food—bonito, mackerel, skipjack, sailfish, marlin, and shark—still await purse seines and long lines. The Bureau of Commercial Fisheries can now process so-called "trash," or unmarketable fish, into a cheap, tasteless, grayish powder called fish protein concentrate (FPC). This powder can thwart the nemesis of young children and pregnant women, protein deficiency. No vast mechanized canneries, home refrigerators or TV mermaids are required to get FPC into hungry bellies. It can be sprinkled on a child's plate of food like salt. American and Japanese interests are already helping Peru's anchovy industry to exploit fish protein concentrate, and our new National Council on Marine Resources has plans for pilot FPC plants in Latin America.

The IATTC, like other regional fish commissions, stands ready to help develop, diversify, and maintain the fisheries that can sustain such revolutionary advances in world nutrition.* The El Nino phenomenon, a coastal intrusion of warm water, drasticly depletes anchovy stocks and, as the Commission notes, "can lead to catastrophes in the economics of several of the South American countries." (Red-tide outbreaks are sometimes associated with El Nino.) Commission scientists are investigating this phenomenon with their South American colleagues in order to predict and combat its occurrence.

Although the skipjack tuna is smaller than the yellow-fin and distributed more widely (skipjack tagged off Mexico are caught off Hawaii), it is more resilient to fishing pressure and thus capable of sustaining a much larger tuna fishery . . . if scientists can better predict its whereabouts for clippers and bolicheros alike. To cultivate skipjack detective skills, the Commission is joining with the Bureau of Commercial Fisheries, Scripps and marine agencies in Peru, Ecuador, Mexico and Chile in an ambitious scientific exploratory program called Eastropac (after Eastern Tropical Pacific).

Ironically, limited funds severely cramp Commission efforts to expand fishery resources. Nations contribute to the Commission in proportion to their commercial fishing activity. The United States, the dominant fishing nation, continually undercuts Commission budget requests, a response that Commission director Kask classifies as "bewildering penuriousness." United States support is less

---

* The Convention establishing the Inter-American Tropical Tuna Commission refers to the possibility of maintaining the population of other kinds of fish taken by tuna fishing vessels, including baitfish like anchoveta.

than one per cent of the value of the United States tuna catch.

Increased support for Commission efforts to expand fishery exploitation, however desirable, will only intensify the need for meeting the crucial problem of resource allocation. The United States presently harvests 90 per cent of the yellowfin; Japan, 3.4 per cent. If American technical prowess leaves CEP nations with a diminishing share of other stocks that come under regulation, these nations will undoubtedly tie a national quota system to conservation regulations and further exercise their two-hundred-mile claim. No country will abide by conservation regulations that freeze the development of its fishery and its economy more than that of other nations.

The regional fish commission, under guidelines agreed to by the fishing nations, could serve to relate socioeconomic as well as biological factors in setting quotas; the burden of conservation could thus be shared on a basis beyond the balance of technical prowess alone.

Such sharing may not appeal to advanced nations, particularly when their fleets have so daringly pioneered fishing grounds. Yet these nations have a responsibility to demonstrate that a common sea truly benefits all, or face the inevitable extension of protectionist sea boundaries. (In Africa, another developing continent, some nations may imitate the CEP claim.) Nor should such sharing be regarded as "blackmail" or "protection money." As Professor James Crutchfield, a noted fishery economist of the University of Washington, observes, "There remains a lingering doubt as to the moral position of the developed nations fully utilizing stocks which are geographically and economically part of the resource base of less developed countries whose need for the product is as great or greater." Do developed nations contribute to their own security by leaving underdeveloped nations farther behind in the dust of progress? Should the potential of the Eastern Tropical Pacific to feed many nations be subordinated to a big-power race to hook, net, web, seine, and otherwise deplete the waters of fish? America's technical and financial involvement in Peru's anchovy industry already accomplishes many of the objectives that so persistently elude the Alliance for Progress and other ambitious foreign-aid programs. (In *International Science and Technology*, April, 1967, John Isaacs of Scripps suggests that America's main role in fishing should be to export know-how, import fish, and use domestic fisheries as a proving ground to solve world hunger. Coral atolls in Micronesia might be converted into tuna pastures that fatten yellowfin and restrict their foraging on anchovies and other valuable herbivores.)

At the same time, such quota and technology sharing will test the devotion of coastal and developing nations to truly effective conservation. Galloping sea sovereignty can never be a substitute for the international range of fishes; only regional fish commissions can effectively encompass this range. Is placing national flags on salmon, whales, and yellowfin really rational?

Ironically, the United States is under considerable pressure to adopt the same protectionist sea boundaries that the CEP nations espouse. Congressman Thomas Pelly (R., Wash.) advocates a get-tough policy with "blackmailing" CEP nations: "I think the thing we ought to do is to send a gunboat down into those waters and protect our fishermen." At the same time, the Washington State Congressman urges that the United States extend its sovereignty over the waters of the continental shelf, a distance of up to 400 miles in some places. The activities of Russian, Japanese, and Korean trawlers inspire the fishermen of New England and the Pacific Northwest to urge that the United States exercise exclusive-fishery jurisdiction to the edge of the continental shelf or two hundred miles out to sea, whichever is farther. America's two most modern and profitable fish fleets, the tuna and Gulf shrimp fleets, warn that such expansion would only rebound on their own distant-water activities. (The Gulf shrimp fleet fishes within nine miles off Mexico. This fishing is now done by the sufferance of Mexico, which duplicated the United States' new twelve-mile fishery limit in early 1967.)

There is considerable speculation that U.S. coastal fishermen suffer as much from their own inefficiency as from the alleged depradations of foreign trawlers. Like the tuna clippers off Latin America, these trawlers often fish stocks that our coastal fishermen have neither the capability nor incentive to harvest. (The Russian trawlers off the Pacific Northwest refrain from fishing salmon.) Yet, as our coastal states cultivate the scientific and economic capability of exploiting adjacent waters as a marine range, the principal rationale of the foreign trawlers—the existence of unexploited stocks—will diminish. Shorn of the overtones of sham conservation, the United States faces a stern test of its devotion to the ocean as an international resource: the development of a fishery policy that at once reflects the true needs of the coastal fishery and the high-seas fishery as well. The temptation to exercise extensive and exclusive coastal jurisdiction is strong; our ocean frontage is such that we would have much less to lose than other fishing nations in retiring behind protectionist sea boundaries.

Yet, as William Neblett of the National Shrimp Congress points out, such a trend could be needless as well as fruitless.

No two areas of our country have identical problems, and there is no magic formula which fits all cases. Should we not consider then, case by case, problem by problem, or better stated, fishery by fishery? If one of our important commercial or sport fisheries is slated for extinction, or even serious depletion, and we have sufficient scientific information to prove it, the United States can declare that particular fishery or stock of fish to be in danger; declare a special interest in it, establish proper regulations concerning it, and tell foreigners to stay out unless those foreigners have a historic interest in the fishery, in which case they are still bound by proper conservation regulations. This, I submit, is proper international law at this minute, and the United States helped to make it so. No artificial limits are necessary to protect a coastal fishery, and to protect salmon, on a mileage basis, you would have to go past the middle of the Pacific Ocean.

By resorting to a "mileage basis" we will also be forfeiting a magnificent opportunity to develop the potential of regional fish commissions and to utilize fully the resources of oceans as rich as the Eastern Tropical Pacific. The United States belongs to nine such commissions, more than any other nation. Future technology may manipulate the size and distribution of fish stocks and thus realize huge increases in fish harvests.* There will be little incentive to apply this advance in the oceans engulfed in technical and political competitions for exclusive use. The nations that join to foster comprehensive regional fish commissions will best implement and share in such fantastic fishery advances.

To ensure a minimum of investment and a maximum of return, such competent commissions may choose to lease out fishing rights. Instead of providing the widest possible access to a fishery, they would seek to provide the most economical access to fishery products. Management, not technology, promises to become the key to successful regional fishery development. Nations which implement sound management in one ocean area will be in a good position to outcompete nations that persist in jockeying for exclusive use of another region, however bountiful.

In a day when Peruvian gunboats hail American tuna clippers, such all-embracing management may not seem to be realistic. Yet a number of world rivals have been practicing it successfully for more than fifty years. In the nineteenth century sealers from Russia, Japan, America, and Canada (then under the British Crown) pursued the fur seal in the chilly, fog-bound waters of the North Pacific Ocean and the Bering Sea. Shortly after purchasing Alaska from Russia in 1867 the United States laid claim to "all the dominion of the United States in the waters of the Bering Sea." The largest fur seal rookeries in the North Pacific area exist on the tiny Pribilof Islands of Alaska. The United States reasoned that these seals were, by extension, the property of the United States while in the surrounding seas and was prepared to accept responsibility for their conservation. At the same time they would have sole control over their exploita-

* Appendix F lists the commissions.

tion. At that time sealing was a far more profitable enterprise than today's salmon or tuna fishing.

Britain was inclined to view the situation differently. In fact, Britain wondered why the United States did not pay rent to the rest of the world for permitting "its" seals to pasture on the open seas. The seal fishery dispute soon escalated to the vessel-seizure stage. Canadian sealers were seized on the high seas or American waters—depending on your choice of governments—and hauled before a territorial court in Sitka. Meanwhile, Japanese sealers poached on the Pribilofs and American sealers poached on the Commander Islands, Russia's seal rookery.

By 1890 Britain informed the United States that future vessel seizures would be opposed by the Royal Navy. The United States then agreed to arbitration before an international tribunal located in Grotius' homeland. Although it recognized the need for seal conservation, the Hague Tribunal refuted the Americanization of the Bering Sea and the right of one nation to dictate conservation on the open seas. The United States was required to compensate Canada for seizure fines amounting to $473,-151. The tribunal then drew up regulations to prohibit Canadians from capturing seals within a sixty-mile-wide zone around the Pribilofs. The conservation regulations were no better than the tribunal's grasp of the complex business of marine management. As the Pacific salmon were to do a century later, the fur seals persisted in crossing this arbitrarily imposed boundary. Canadian sealers, not content with this over-the-border flow, exchanged the British flag for the flag of nations not bound by the tribunal's sixty-mile zone, such as Japan. This inspired the U.S. House of Representatives to pass a bill to slaughter Pribilof seals en masse and thus end the dispute for good. The Senate demurred.

Actually, the aim of this bill had been nearly accomplished. The 1867 estimate of 4.7 million seals had dropped by 1910 to a count of one hundred twenty-five thousand. This swift decline finally encouraged Britain, Japan, Russia, and the United States to accept the challenge of devising a joint Pacific fur-seal management program. Scientific inquiries discovered that the killing of a female seal was the most wasteful, for three lives might be involved: the female herself, an unborn pup, and an unweaned pup. On the other hand, bull seals who lost out in the competition for twenty-cow harems could be killed without sapping the seal stocks. It is difficult to tell a cow from an expendable bull at sea. An effective harvest could be conducted only on land, where excess bulls could be segregated, herded, and systematically clubbed.

In the 1911 Fur Seal Convention killing was limited to the rookery islands of Russia, Japan, and the United States. The warship of one nation could inspect the vessel of another on suspicion of sealing in the Okhotsk, Bering, Kamchatka, Japan, and North Pacific waters. For refraining from sea sealing Canada and Japan (whose rookery was small) were to receive up to fifteen per cent shares in the seal harvests. These two countries also received ten thousand dollars indemnity for their unemployed sealers and a two hundred thousand dollar advance for their signatures on the Convention. A joint commission administers the Convention today.

The United States has rebuilt the Pribilof stocks and now leases out processing rights to maximize economic return. In 1912 three thousand seven hundred sixty-four seal skins were harvested; in 1941, ninety-five thousand. In this period Canada received some 1.7 million dollars simply for refraining from sealing. Seals are now processed for oil and mink food as well as for their pelts.

The rebuilt seal herds now compete with fishermen for salmon and other finny tidbits, but the seal commission, in keeping with its comprehensive spirit, can regulate herd size to control predation.

The ease of management and the declining commercial importance of seals account in part for the remarkable harmony in the Fur Seal Convention. These factors notwithstanding, the Convention still serves to reaffirm strongly the relevance of the common-sea concept to an exploited ocean. No other marine creature has been placed under such rewarding management, both biological and economic. This is being accomplished without resort to two-hundred-mile sea boundaries, unilateral conservation, and technological races.

The high-seas fishery vividly exemplifies the dangers of the ocean technology's potential to inspire a return to the deceptive security of exclusive ocean use. The Geneva Conference on the Law of the Sea, which attempted to grapple with the problems of fishery exploitation, also tried to come to terms with those of seabed exploitation. President Truman's Proclamation extended national sovereignty over the adjacent continental shelf. The Conference's Convention on the Continental Shelf adds "or, beyond that limit, to where the depth of the superjacent waters admits of the exploitation of the natural resources of the said areas." This magnanimous extension helps foster an ocean competition every bit as intense as fishing and considerably more ominous.

18.

The Military Ocean

SIR FRANCIS BACON's admonition—"He that commands the sea is at great liberty, and may take as much and as little of war as he will"—has not always found favor in this century. First, the heavier-than-air machine threatened to put world navies out of business. "Navies are no longer the lords of the sea," proclaimed Major de Seversky, an early air enthusiast who referred to aircraft carriers as "floating hangars." Who needed control of the ocean when one had control of the ultimate in high ground, the air? Although World War II proved Bacon more contemporary than de Seversky, the denigration of sea power continued. Instant war, packaged in land-based missiles, seemed destined to fossilize aircraft carriers and battleships.

Yet today admirals rather than Air Force generals are "in" before congressional appropriation committees. Military scholars at RAND bone up on Bacon and Mahan instead of de Seversky and other advocates of air power. A new form of technology now makes the Navy fashionable in Moscow as well as Washington, so fashionable that the concept of control of the ocean is being supplanted by one of uncertain but rather provocative dimensions: *occupation* of the ocean.

The cause of this stir, the submarine, has a checkered history. In its early stages it inspired much official fear. In 1805 Robert Fulton, sitting in his candle-lit, copper submarine *Nautilus*, sank the British brig *Dorothy*. The sinking, effected by planting a charge on the brig's hull, was staged for an audience that included Prime Minister William Pitt. The audience was thoroughly impressed. By merely slipping below the sea a metal cylinder gained concealment, surprise, and an armor that no other war vessel could boast. But the British Admiralty was not buying. Admiral Lord St. Vincent calculated that England had more to lose than gain by promoting watertight cylinders: "Pitt was the greatest fool that ever existed to encourage a mode of warfare which those who commanded the seas did not want, and which, if successful, would at once deprive them of it."

Moreover, the sub later disappointed its already ambivalent champions. It could not go down very far beneath the sea—thus rendering itself a good echo surface for ping-ponging sonar—or for very long. The need for oxygen forced it to surface periodically or to otherwise advertise its presence with a "feather," the wake of its snorkel. In fact, subs spent most of their time on the surface, a situation that fostered a danger besides detection. Because of their low silhouette and sluggish maneuverability, they were constantly being rammed by tug boats, tankers, friendly destroyers, and other unsuspecting sub killers. In these collisions a submarine's principal armor—the ocean depths—was of little use.

Submerged or surfaced, the awkward sub generally shunned encounters with escort destroyers, aircraft carriers, and cruises. Sub skippers, other than John Wayne, found Admiral Nelson's stirring dictum "No captain can do very wrong who places his ships alongside the enemy"—suicidal in practice. Encounters with lonely merchant ships, troop carriers, damaged cruisers and unprotected convoys were preferred. This choice in adversaries, led naturally to notoriety. In Hollywood movies U-boat skippers seemed to torpedo tankers only in order to be able to surface and machine-gun oil-smeared survivors, thrashing about in the numbing Atlantic waters. The sub became the craven sneak of the ocean—the tool of the weak naval power—able to maraud but unable to wrest control of the sea from the big boys topside.

It is nuclear power that transforms the submarine into the navy's very salvation. No application of this power—nuclear power plants, Project Plowshares, or nuclear merchant vessels—has so upgraded a military capability. A nuclear reactor does not burn oxygen. Man, the only user of oxygen aboard, can be supplied by electrolysis of sea water into O^2 and by scrubbers that keep the air, as Madison Avenue might have it, "country fresh." Thus the naval sneak becomes a true submarine, able to enjoy the military luxuries of the undersea almost indefinitely. Refueling is required only every four years —the life span of the sub's reactor cores. Navies have not enjoyed such stamina since ships depended solely on wind in their sails. Liberated from the sea surface, the nuclear sub can cruise beneath gales, storm waves, *chubascos*, ice, and other traditional obstructions to ocean travel. The nuclear sub sheds the sharp, sharklike hull of conventional subs for one that is rounded and whale-shaped altogether more in keeping with undersea hydrodynamics. Nuclear subs can now match the fastest surface ships, and their new pressure-resistant hulls allow them to dive three and four times deeper than World War II models before reaching crushing depth. There is no better concealment or armor than a fifteen-hundred-foot layer of ocean. Radar, searchlights, and the bow of a tugboat no longer threaten discovery and destruction.

The nuclear missile provides the sub with a weapon equal to its upgraded performance. Instead of notching ship silhouettes on a torpedo tube, a recent cartoon portrayed a sailor busily inscribing on a Polaris missile the names Moscow, Peking, and Selma, Alabama. A submarine submerged can now exercise a capability the Air Force once monopolized—strategic bombing—with far greater invulnerability than a SAC bomber or a stationary missile system. Today, the Air Force is considering the possibility of moving its missiles out of silos and placing them on launchers that can crawl along the ocean bottom. To submariners this move suggests that the Air Force may soon obstruct navigation. Major de Seversky would undoubtedly be shocked, Sir Francis Bacon reassured.

The fate of military efforts to neutralize an enemy nuclear submarine underscores its awesome, near-perfect nature. Antisubmarine warfare groups are a distilled blend of naval power, which includes aircraft carriers, swift destroyers, helicopters, jets, and even submarines. Yet ASW forces resemble a detective who has his eyes blindfolded, his nostrils plugged up, and his hands gloved. Only one sense remains to detect, identify and aim at an adversary: hearing. The ocean is a good, if sometimes deceptive sound-conductor, and nuclear subs, obligingly enough, are noisier than their conventional counterparts. Sonar, which now comes in active (echo ranging) and passive (listening) modes, enhances the power of the ear. A helicopter pilot may dunk a hydrophone into the sea and hear a wrench drop in a submarine below, but the range of a hydrophone requires that the pilot be near the sub in the first place. If the Pacific Ocean were the size of Lake Erie, this would pose no problem. Moreover, unfortunately, there are many other noisemakers in the ocean, including porpoises, snapping shrimp and the propellers of ASW task forces. In fact, the ocean is so noisy that computers must be programmed with sound signatures to handle the task of weeding out false targets. Even a well programmed computer cannot detect a sub that may be running "silent," engines off and wrenches well in hand.

Because of its limitations, passive sonar is utilized principally in closing in on an unidentified contact or serving as an electronic sentry on a nation's continental shelf or in narrow ocean passages.

Active sonar can be effective, whether the sub is silent or indiscreet. The operator of active sonar does not have to put up with a lot of noises. Instead, he has to cope with a great many other surfaces besides sub hulls that bounce back pings—whales, schools of tuna, sea mounts, and "the deep scattering layer" (light-sensitive organisms that rise up and down in vast vertical migrations). Thermoclimes (sharp temperature gradients) and variable salinity conditions can also bend sound waves and hamper the deadly business of tracking a sub by triangulation. Canny submarine captains often park behind sea mounts, in underwater canyons, or beneath the thermoclime.

If ASW forces can manage to penetrate the deceit of the ocean and unmask an enemy contact, a depth charge can then be dropped. In World War II this concussive weapon had to be exploded as close to the sub as thirty-five yards, a degree of accuracy that allowed Hollywood directors to prolong submarine death scenes. Now a new nuclear depth bomb, *Lulu*, carries a yield of one and one quarter kilotons, thus allowing for errors on the order of thousands of yards. Yet such latitude still may not be enough. However noisy, a nuclear sub can be long gone—in depth as well as distance—after a telltale ping. Nuclear subs can hear, too. They possess passive sonar for detecting and gaging active sonar. In the days of sail landsmen allegedly lured sailing ships into rocks with decoy lights in a scavenging practice called "Jibber the Kibber." In a twentieth century twist a submarine may send out false target decoys. In the near future a sub may pass directly by a probing ping, confident that its rubberized hull will absorb the noise.

Instead of baiting its opponent, a sub may decide to step up the action. Nuclear subs still carry torpedoes, and, unlike conventional subs, they can now outmaneuver surface ships and give an inquisitive jet a zigzag run for its money. Subs can maintain this pace oblivious to the gales, storm waves, and fog that may afflict its pursuers topside.

Recently two conventional subs engaged in a submerged mock battle off San Diego. The exercise came to an abrupt halt when the two subs bumped into one another. Miraculously enough, superstructures alone were involved and the tender hulls escaped unscathed. At a press conference, the commander of Sub Flotilla 1 explained how four thousand tons of sophisticated metal could collide, and his explanation epitomizes the challenge of undersea warfare. "Down there, it's like two people in a dark room with baseball bats trying to hit each other." Corroborates oceanographer Roger Revelle, "The terrible opacity of the oceans makes the business of fighting submarines a grotesque kind of jungle warfare."

There is little doubt just who the undersea lion in this warfare really is. Recently the U.S. *Naval Institute Proceedings* ran an essay entitled "The Submarine's Long Shadow." Its aggressive pronuclear sub stance inspired the author's naval peers to vent charges of near-heresy in the Letters to the Editor column. The editor, however, honored the article as the *Proceedings*' prize essay of 1966. The navies of the world, not just their submarines, are faced with the possible prospect of going underwater or else being delivered there by torpedo. The fears of Admiral Lord St. Vincent are finally being realized.

The chief limitation on the capability of nuclear subs is man himself. As the nicknames "pig boat" and "sewer pipe" suggest, little attention was paid to the standards of habitability aboard World War II subs. One scientist characterized the interior of the sub as infested by "a whole spectrum of stinks." The primary agent was the humid temperatures that could hit ninety-three degrees. Perspiration would run off the bodies of men like water, fill shoes, and create slippery puddles on the deck.

Space was at a premium. The entire sub served as a larder. Flour sacks were sandwiched between piping; canned peas were stuffed under torpedos. Bunks were also crammed between torpedoes; men on different shifts shared the same clammy bunk in a practice called "hot bunking." The piston throb of the engines and the nervewracking dripping from pressure-weakened piping sometimes made sheer exhaustion a prerequisite for sleep. Men who turned in their sleep often raised welts on their foreheads. A torpedo bunk was no place for restless sleepers, much less a sleepwalker. To awaken in this dank world was to face waiting in line for the one wash basin and two toilets in the enlisted men's washroom. A sparse salt shower was living it up.

Amid this tight, sweaty existence a careless elbow in the ribs while passing in the corridor could spark a screaming brawl. There was, however, an even more pathetic casualty of sub living than the battered victim of an accidental elbow. The sub's wallowing on the surface—plus its inability to observe a steady horizon—fostered a maximum of sea sickness, and there is no ship's rail on a submarine. The U-boat crews who nearly choked off England's shipping were not, in reality, maniacal machine gunners of torpedo victims. Like their American and British counterparts, they stoically endured extended periods of human wretchedness, often climaxed by the excruciating gap between a probing ping and a concussive depth charge.

Today nuclear subs stay down for two months at a time, instead of for just a day or so. The crew is entrusted with weapons that can devastate a nation instead of a single ship. Such circumstances have inspired a near-revolution in submarine habitability. A nuclear sub now reminds one more of a modest cruise liner than a sewer pipe. The sub itself is three stories high. Sleeping quarters resemble the green-curtained Pullman sections in railroad cars. Men can turn comfortably in their sleep. They can also turn on a reading lamp. The sub's motionless ride makes sea sickness a thing of the unhappy past. Air-conditioning (for the electronic equipment as well as the men) eliminates sweat-filled shoes. There are automatic clothes washers that do not require a coin. The bulkheads sport plastic wallpaper. "Officers' Country" is paneled in walnut-grained aluminum. Washrooms boast electric-shaving lather dispensers, hot-air hand dryers, and, as an ex-pig boater noted, "even urinal stalls."

A sub has the same aura of efficiency as a computerized control center for electric power or municipal sewage. A navigator no longer shoots the stars; he scans gyro compasses. Instead of a handsome wooden wheel, the helmsman operates an airplanelike stick that can send the sub into forty-five degree dives. He does not guide on starboard lights, bell buoys, or sunset horizons. Like his colleagues, he heeds dials. As Melville wrote of the hodders, the men below the whaler's decks, "They may circumnavigate the world fifty times, and they see about as much of it as Jonah did in the whale's belly. They do not even hear the cry of the sea gulls."

Submariners worry about blown fuses, pipes that weep, and high-pressure leaks. Although not so romantic as a Conrad typhoon, mechanical failures can be every bit as fatal. Water jetting from a high-pressure leak can knock the wind out of a helmsman and shatter a control panel. It was a piping failure that apparently sent the *Thresher* to its fate.

Mental stress has come to replace physical discomfort. Because passing the time can become a major occupation, chefs trained in America's best hotel kitchens prepare lobster, beef stroganoff, and other dishes that foster a sense of anticipation. In between the gourmet meals is "soup down," a coffee break that includes cheese and salami. This lavish undersea diet creates its own problem: overweight. Consulting psychiatrists recommend stationary bicycle races or the installation of a handball court. The Navy has settled for a barbell gym.

To the century-old ancestors of this sailor—the men who were impressed on blood ships, who subsisted on salt junk, danderfunk, and slumgullion, who were cursed by calms as well as hurricanes, who regarded the inside of the ocean as a grave—such a life would be an undreamed-of Fiddler's Green. And this is perhaps the most significant achievement of the nuclear submarine. A surface ship was and still is an alien in the ocean environment, always with an eye on the barometer and the distance from port; only a nuclear sub can become a part of that environment. It alone makes the ocean habitable. Future submarines with a critical atomic pile for a power source will convey scientists, surveyors, and deep-sea miners. Fishermen in white lab coats will peer through glass hulls, spy a yellowfin, trail it, and set a net underneath a teeming school. The merchant submarine will tow cargo pods well below the turmoil of the air-ocean interface to deposit them on the continental shelf, thus preventing port tie-ups. The submarine is the vehicle that will open up the ocean and transport and shelter working communities throughout its enormous expanse.

While raising such a promising prospect, the nuclear sub also presents a grave problem: the possibility of an ocean arms race which could severely retard peaceful habitation of the oceans. The military prowess of the nuclear sub alone would probably guarantee such an ominous trend, but other developments in undersea technology add momentum to it. Moored sea mines once defended harbors from bold submarines and coastlines from amphibious assaults. Today mines can be an offensive weapon as well. A submersible vehicle could slink into a deep underwater canyon that heads at a major port and deposit a nuclear mine. A sailor aboard an oil tanker in the Panama Canal could kick overboard a dirty container housing a similar device. Sediment and encrusting animals can render its fiberglass (nonmagnetic) housing immune to detecting equipment. Meanwhile, telemetry equipment a continent away might control its ultimate fate. Mines as well as submarines can render the ocean's opacity a fearsome thing. A nation could have its coastal cities systematically blown up, yet not know where to aim the diplomatic or ballistic protests. For a nation with an embryonic nuclear capability but no sleek delivery system, the long-distance mine may have special appeal. Nor need the appeal of "anonymous" warfare be limited to small nations with big grudges. As U.S. Navy Commander J. A. Meacham observes in an article in the *Proceedings*, "In very specialized cases, such as clandestine support of another country, mines can easily be manufactured which could bear no trace of their origin. I do not propose this in a specific case, but I can easily imagine situations in which we would like to sink somebody's ships without being tagged as the villain of the piece." No nation can ignore the military implications of undersea technology.

Russia's sudden emergence as a sea power testifies eloquently to the convincing prowess of undersea technology. There are few Nelsons at Trafalgar in Russian naval annals. For a naval victory the Russians sometimes go all the way back to 1714. The Swedes had bottled up Peter the Great's fleet in a Baltic gulf. Peter decided to push his blockaded fleet across an isthmus on rollers, but nine small Swedish vessels held a strategic channel. The vessels were eventually neutralized, but it took ninety-five Russian galleys to pull off the victory at Gangut. Russia's naval defeats have, however, been resounding. In the Russo-Japanese War the intrepid Admiral Togo bottled up seven Russian battleships in Port Arthur. On the other side of the continent the Czar appealed to the spirit of Gangut and dispatched a large relief force. At the Battle of Tsushima, Togo annihilated the relief force in one of history's most decisive battles.

Russia's naval record has been largely fated by her geography. With the Panama Canal, America's naval fleets have access to all American sea frontiers. Russia's sea fronts—the Black, Baltic, Arctic, and North Pacific—are isolated from one another and no single canal can remedy this isolation. To complicate matters most Russian passages to the open ocean are icebound or controlled by countries quite conscious of Russia's geographical limitations. "Denmark may be described as the doorkeeper of the Baltic," notes Commander J. V. Stilling, Royal Danish Navy, in The Soviet Navy. "These circumstances impose upon Denmark a moral obligation to keep a constant watch on the western Baltic. . . . Any appreciable attempt to filter Russian submarines through the Danish Straits into the open sea would be tantamount to preparation for war."

In the same book an anonymous Turkish officer quotes an old proverb. " 'If you will not be able to shut the gate again, do not raise the latch.' Turkey keeps a sharp eye on that gate (the Dardanelles). She is the dam that holds back the Russian tide."

Frustrated by geography, Russia has traditionally concentrated its military resources on the army. In sizing up East-West confrontations, military experts invariably talk in terms of the land beast versus the sea beast, the elephant versus the whale. The Russians have often been willing to accept this classification. At a Moscow diplomatic reception in the late 1950's an American Air Force general looked out a window and saw Russian sailors rowing a boat in a park pond. "There is our Navy," declared a voice. The speaker was the then-premier, Nikita Khrushchev.

Today Russian premiers no longer knock the Navy. Russia's enthusiasm for nuclear subs far exceeds any psychic need to keep up with the Pentagon. The nuclear sub, with its ability to glide beneath obstructive ice, to avoid frequent refueling runs through the Turkish or Danish straits, and to roam the open ocean, gives Russia the chance to contend for command of the sea without even possessing a powerful surface fleet.

That this opportunity comes at a time when one big missile exchange might make command of the sea academic has not prevented Russia, like America, from building up its undersea capabilities. The search for invulnerability is apparently endless and not easily deterred by such factors as cost. (An American nuclear sub costs forty-three million dollars—one hundred thirty-six million with sixteen Polaris missiles.) Although America has a headstart in nuclear sub technology and production, Russia is not far behind and already has missile-firing atomic subs stationed one thousand miles off our Pacific and Atlantic coasts.* (With numerous conventional subs, Russia has the largest sub fleet in the world, more than four hundred. Interestingly enough, Russia pawned its older subs off on China in the last decade, and India and Egypt have been its prime recip-

* "Soviet Missile Subs Patrol Off U.S.," *Technology Week* (April 4, 1966). Report attributed to "high-level U.S. Navy officials."

ients in the sixties.) Russia's military undersea efforts
are not confined to nuclear subs. Notes Raymond Garthoff, a military scholar at RAND, "Admiral Vladimirsky
has explicitly pointed to the possibilities of delivering
mines and underwater torpedos with nuclear warheads
into the harbors of major enemy ports and naval bases."
Even the literary set is being drafted into the naval
buildup. A "little" review recently urged writers to de-
vote more attention to naval matters, for "a great Navy
has a right to great literature." (Based on history, the
writers have their work cut out for them.)

Undersea technology thus enables the elephant to become a proficient swimmer, so proficient that the whale
is deeply concerned. Observes one U.S. naval officer in
the *Proceedings*, "If we consider the sea lanes as the
streets of the world, there are armed, unpredictable men
on the prowl in the neighborhood." Retired Admiral
Jerauld Wright remarks, "Lose the Atlantic and we fight
the war alone, with the Iron Curtain at our 10-fathom
curve."

Today the U.S. Navy is quite literally installing itself
in the ocean. Since detection of subs by hunter-killer
groups is so depressingly random, the Navy plants hy-
drophonic listening "gardens" on the sea bed, sonobuoy
grids on the surface, and electronic tower islands on sea
mounts to bug the ocean . . . and hope that Russian subs
remain noisy. The Navy also investigates the possibility
of magnetic, scent, heat, and laser detection. Although it
is not especially confident about its ability to make the
oceans transparent, the Navy feels compelled at least
to try.

There is a well-grounded suspicion that submarine
technology will progress faster than the technology of
ASW forces. Under a Navy contract, General Dynamics
—Convair has found the concept of a sub-plane feasible,
so feasible in fact that RAND, the Air Force's premier
think factory, is diligently studying the identical concept.
The sub-plane envisioned by Convair would submerge
by controlled flooding of the wings and the tail. Before

takeoff the wings and tail would be emptied, the sub-plane would surface, and three jet engines would handle the rest. Submariners would finally see more of the world than Jonah.

ASW forces count heavily on their ability to track hostile submarines from their port of origin. By originating from inland airports, a sub-plane could cancel out this advantage. Besides learning to fly, future submarines are being groomed to carry midget attack submarines, to land Marine battalions, haul Army cargo, sow nuclear mines, and, in general, to combine all the arts of war within one steel hull. Interchangeable bows will facilitate abrupt role changes. Instead of making a circle to turn around, future subs may simply go into reverse, move sideways, and otherwise sidestep ASW measures. The arms race can turn the ocean into an elaborate stage for costly and obsessive military gymnastics.

In the midst of World War II Bernard Brodie, a prominent naval theorist, declared, "The naval defense of the United States has been simplified by the submarine. As a weapon in the hands of the enemy, it can exercise small effect on the American economy of war." Today defense against this weapon dominates national efforts in oceanographic exploitation. Of antisubmarine warfare, the *Naval Officer's Guide* admits quite frankly, "The cost in money alone will be enormous." Vice Admiral Charles Martell, director of ASW programs, notes, "Oceanography is the right arm of ASW." Naval dominance of national oceanographic resources occurs across the board. Although pioneering man's free swimming ability in the ocean depths has great scientific and economic import, it is the Navy that runs this nation's man-in-the-sea program (Sealab). The speed and all-weather capability of hydrofoil technology has similar importance, but it is the Navy, exploring the theory that hydrofoils may make the surface fleet a match for subs, that again monopolizes research in this area. Although much of America's offshore, including the continental shelf, remains a mysterious resource, the Navy dispatches large scientific explorations to the East Siberian Sea and other less mysterious waters.*

Often unclassified in the past, more and more naval research promises to be as classified as the proprietary data of offshore oil explorations. Undersea warfare is becoming all-encompassing in nature, and there is nothing like a "classified" stamp to impress the Bureau of the Budget Wilbert Chapman told a Congressional committee recently.

The Navy is well aware of the benefits to be gained from operations of a multiresource nature. Merchant marine ships carry mobile Naval lab vans which record thermoclimes and other useful information for antisubmarine warfare. A distant-fishing fleet like the tuna fleet may be recruited as a surveillance instrument.

The greatest impact of the military ocean effort may be on the ocean's political character. The possibility of ocean occupation is being raised in various guises. As previously noted, the Convention on the Continental Shelf declares that a coastal state exercises sovereignty over the geographical continental shelf "or, beyond that limit, to where the depth of the superjacent waters admits of the exploitation of the natural resources of the said areas." "Superjacent" and "exploitation" can be open-ended terms. "Who knows, maybe our continental shelf extends out to the East China Sea," observed an Interior official in charge of leasing submarine lands. The emerging ability to inhabit the ocean now fosters speculation over schemes that will inevitably test the flexibility of these terms. "It may be necessary, for public relations reasons, to establish a clear-cut goal, similar to the race to put a man on the moon, in order to get us off dead center of the ocean use program," Dr. Wilbert Chapman told a Congressional committee recently. "That goal would be the occupation of a section of the deep seabed on behalf of the United States. . . . That would take a little of the shine off the moon adventure."

* Appendix C shows the Navy's fiscal hold on Federal oceanography.

Under the weight of the ocean arms race naval officials are considering occupation in terms other than those of public relations. "If present indications of mineral deposits in these broad ocean areas are realized, the resolution of these legal rights will become a practical necessity, involving, if necessary, a military presence," observes John Craven, chief scientist in the Navy's office of Special Projects. "Nor is it unrealistic to conjecture that in the future the asseration of property rights in sea basins or on 'strategic ridges' (territories constituting more than three times that of the dry land counterparts) could provide a basis for modification of the full freedom of the sea which has been so widely cherished for nearly a thousand years." In a *Proceedings* article titled "Sea Power and the Sea Bed," Craven asserts that "modification of the full freedom of the seas" need not necessarily be restricted to the occupied seabed. "The right to regulate the jettison of material over occupied areas of the seabed, the right to regulate traffic above and around occupied areas of the seabed, and the right to discriminate between peaceable and belligerent transit over occupied areas of the seabed may well result as emoluments of sovereignty."

Prospective modification of the freedom of the seas can become less an effort to effect economic exploitation than to gain—or deny—military advantage. "I suggest that the law of the sea, in many instances right out on our Continental Shelf, is in a position now of where the fastest gun in the submarine world may very well be the most important owner in the undersea world," declared Congressman Richard Hanna before the House Subcommittee on Oceanography. Before the same Subcommittee, Lt. Commander Don Walsh, a bathyscaphe pioneer who unfurled a ceremonial U.S. flag in the Challenger Deep off Guam, said the "principal issue" involved in our ocean activities should be "the projection of our national sovereignty into the world ocean. . . . I mean sea power not only as a military projection of our national power, but also a strong merchant marine, a strong fishing industry, and a strong resources industry involved in the oceans; but principally it is a projection of our national power."

Recently, the Navy dropped a fourteen-foot tower into the ocean off California. The tower was later retrieved and the condition of more than thirteen hundred sample building materials carefully studied. The *Naval Research Review* reports, "With the information obtained through the Deep Ocean Program, engineers will be able to design and emplace or construct a variety of facilities beneath the sea, such as fuel caches, supply depots, refueling stations, submarine repair facilities, nuclear weapon shelters, utility systems and power generators." Today Westinghouse and General Dynamics are conducting studies for the Navy on a "manned undersea station." The technology and the ideology to garrison the ocean thus converge. The Navy finds itself considering partial occupation of the great medium the United States champions as free and open. It is not only Peruvians and Ecuadorians who talk of "modification of the full freedom of the seas."

The Navy's influence over the ocean policy of the United States, an influence which could be momentous, can foster sharp exchanges over just how far this influence ought to extend. In testifying before the hearings on the Sea-Grant College proposal, Dr. Victor Basiuk identified himself as an associate professor of political science at Case Institute of Technology. "I am also a consultant on the Naval Long-Range Objectives Group, Office of the Chief of Naval Operations, Navy Department. The views expressed in this statement, however, are my own and do not necessarily represent those of the institutions with which I am affiliated." Dr. Basiuk recommended that the legislative language justifying the Sea-Grant concept include an allusion to the United States " 'as the leader of the free world.' This would give a hint of policy orientation with respect to foreign affairs." Dr. Basiuk elaborated on the hint. "Our civilian oceanic R.&D. can proceed much further and much faster if the interests of the U.S. Navy are considered and naval cooperation is obtained. The mining of the ocean bottom can provide our submarines with stations and sources of supply. Nonmilitary presence in the oceans can in turn provide the Navy with navigational assistance, information, and can deny footholds to a potential enemy."

The chairman of the hearings, Senator Claiborne Pell, thanked Dr. Basiuk for his testimony and then declared, "Actually, the thoughts you have advanced have great interest. I think they would change the purpose of the bill, however, because this is not in any way a cold-war bill or national-strategy bill." Dr. Basiuk then denied trying "to make this a battleground of anything." Senator Pell responded, "I understand, and I fully understand the strength of your views and, as I said earlier, I know of your own background as a professor at the Naval War College and I appreciate what you are saying. The thrust of the bill, however, is more, as I said earlier, to increase our number of fishermen and miners and possibly to make seaweed of greater use to the manufacturers and farmers of this country, and things of that sort."

This exchange suggests two sharply divergent points of view regarding American emphasis on ocean exploitation. One side would pursue exploitation on a scientific and economic basis, shorn of military one-upmanship; the other would like to incorporate economic activities into the construction of paramilitary mining camps, the erection of nuclear weapon depots, the occupation of strategic ridges, the denial of undersea footholds to other nations, and other ambitious projections of national sovereignty. Champions of the first view could operate within the "common-property" nature of freedom of the seas. Proponents of the more militant stance could alter this doctrine on the premise that it no longer pays off and that the United States had better raise the flag a thousand fathoms down before someone else does. A choice between these viewpoints becomes increasingly important; the evolution of undersea technology will not await political consensus. Because the pressures for a military ocean are often based on Russia's suspected intentions, a look at her over-all ocean strategy is relevant here.

Undoubtedly, Russia, as a world power, feels it can do no less than become a rival sea power. Yet Russian naval efforts by no means dominate the country's over-all ocean effort. Although the United States formed a National Council on Marine Resources and Engineering Development in 1966, Russia's National Council for the Utilization of the Resources of the Sea has for a number of years been fostering a broad appreciation and application of ocean technology. Russia possesses the first nonmilitary research submarine,* and her appreciation of the ocean challenge is not limited to installing observatory portholes in war-surplus subs. A traditional hirer of cargo vessels, Russia has, within the decade, surpassed the United States in merchant-marine tonnage and now stands second only to Japan. (This, unfortunately, is not too substantial an achievement. As Dr. Chapman observes, "Our merchant marine is noted as our sickest industry.") The husbanding of a merchant marine that does not rely on World War II hulls is surpassed by an even more significant accomplishment. In less than two decades Russia has developed from a coastal fishing country into the world's third-ranking high-seas fishing nation.

Instead of fishing, Russian trawlers are often accused of loitering around New London to record sound signatures of Polaris subs, to smuggle liberation arms to Lumumba's heirs, to destroy naval sonobuoys, refuel subs, plan undersea spy sites, and otherwise to cloak Russian military maneuvers. These charges are often made by individuals, such as coastal fishermen, interested in promoting an extension of U.S. territorial waters. As William Neblett, executive director of the National Shrimp Congress observes, "I submit that we fishermen should leave matters of defense to the Defense Department and not continue to theorize on the radar installations and depth

* The Bureau of Commercial Fisheries now plans to design a similar one.

recorders of foreign vessels. Any Russians who want to know the depth of our coastal waters can walk into a store and buy a U.S. hydrographic chart. The closer you come to shore, or in our bays and ports, the more detailed are these charts." Russia is certainly as aware of the intelligence-gathering capacity of civilian vessels as the U.S. Navy. Yet the principal motivation for ocean fishing lies elsewhere. Russian agriculture, due to a harsh climate and poor planning, continually fails to fulfill its five-year plans. Another food source is in trouble. While rich in anadromous and inland fish stocks, Russia is at times more adept than the United States in polluting, damming, and otherwise destroying salmon and sturgeon nurseries.

By investing tremendous amounts of national resources to realize the yield of the sea, Russia now exploits fish stocks that other nations have been too poor —or too rich—to recognize. Thus the bountiful hake, saury, pollack, and anchovy stocks off our Pacific Coast are finally being gleaned by graduates of the Astrakhan and Vladivostok Technical Fishery Institutes.

Russia landed one million metric tons of fish in 1950, six times that figure in 1965. By the end of the decade Russia will be the top fishing nation in the world. (America will have to exert sizable efforts just to remain fifth. It was second to Japan in 1954.) It would be asking a lot even of a Communist society to consume such production largely as a front for military chicanery. Despite the tremendous investment in exploiting the ocean's feeding capacity, Russia has confirmed an economic fact: it is cheaper to harvest the sea than the land.

Russian fishery efforts have been reduced to a protein race in the inevitable cold war style. Accordingly, Russia is aiming to wield great economic power by cornering the world's fish. There may be a protein race in the future, but two factors must be recognized. First, the present state of Russian agriculture is such that Russians largely consume their own fish production. Second, such a race would be won less by Russian efforts than by America's lack of effort. Rather than develop our own coastal fish stocks, we import half our fish consumption and thus become the world's number one fish importer.

Russia's huge investment in the ocean's food potential influences its ocean policy. It cannot afford to jeopardize this investment by depleting fish stocks or by encouraging coastal nations to proclaim two-hundred-mile fishing zones. "If there is an international fisheries commission in the area being fished that they can join, the Russians join in it and wholeheartedly participate in its work," observes Dr. Chapman, who is well acquainted with the history of such commissions. When Russian trawlers began fishing off Oregon in 1966, coastal fishermen, much like their counterparts in Ecuador and Peru, leveled charges of "fish plunder." The Department of State then invited Russia to engage in fish talks that might lead to regulations. The Bureau of Commercial Fisheries admitted quite frankly, "The foreign fishing activity off our Pacific coast is so far legal, the past performance of the U.S.S.R. indicates she will honor conservation agreements . . . the best action we can take under the present circumstances is to develop and promote a vigorous U.S. fishing industry and to conduct the necessary research and keep currently abreast of the condition of the exploited fish populations." Thomas Scott, department head of Fisheries at Oregon State University observed, "As a consequence of inadequate funds to support basic research on fishes of the sea, we are not prepared to engage in effective discussion with foreign powers for the purpose of establishing a sound treaty to conserve our marine fishery. The Russians may know more about some segments of our fishery resource than we know ourselves." (This observation, appropriately enough, was made in support of the sea-grant legislation.) Despite the lack of sound evidence, Russia acceded to the State Department's request and entered into negotiations that, as Mr. Scott indicates, must be embarrassingly one-sided, scientifically speaking. (The negotiations concluded in February, 1967, with Russia agreeing to minimize fishing gear conflicts, regulate waste discharges, abstain from fishing certain waters beyond the United States' twelve-mile fishery jurisdiction and exchange fishery research data and fleet visits.)

In fishery relations with underdeveloped countries Russia eagerly participates in cooperative ventures, helping to establish a navigation academy in Indonesia, a tuna fishery in Senegal, and fisheries in Cuba, Ceylon, Ghana, and the Congo.

Russia is, however, by no means entirely obliging in the ocean arena. A member of the International Whaling Commission, Russia (along with Japan) delayed a much-needed moratorium on whaling, ostensibly for scientific reasons, but more probably to meet the bullish requirements of a five-year plan. It still persists in claiming a half-million-square-mile arm of the Pacific—the Sea of Okhotsk—while fishing in the Gulf of Alaska.

Such hypocrisy—a not uncommon quality in ocean politics—may diminish as Russia's stake in wide access to the high seas increases. This becomes critical for any nation investing heavily in ocean technology. An ocean rent by expansive territorial waters, strategic ridges, seabed grabs, and other projections of national sovereignty would jeopardize the fullest exercise of such technology. Russia's efforts in the sea thus tend toward a type of control built on the shared use concept. Notes Dr. Schaefer:

> Traditionally, the strategy of the United States with respect to the high seas has been mainly concerned with the freedom of our maritime commerce and the operation of our naval fleets. . . . However, in the modern world, the direct application of military force is becoming more and more difficult and less and less fruitful. Control of the sea by other means is of increasingly greater importance. Other than military force, the important element of control of the sea is its use. The main ways in which nations have used the high seas in the past are for marine transportation and for fisheries. . . . Unfortunately, our merchant fleet dwindles and our fishing fleets are decadent, while the fleets of other nations, including the Soviet, flourish.

Ocean technology geared to economic exploitation may thus serve to accomplish a more worthwhile control of the sea in a more profitable and diplomatic man-

244 THE FRAIL OCEAN

ner than technology geared to military and paramilitary advantage. Systematic occupation of the seabed could become particularly self-defeating. If an ambitious country raises the flag on a sea mount a thousand miles distant from its coast under the guise of retrieving magnesium nodules, it serves to justify similar claims by other nations. This boomerang potential suggests restraint in automatically equating use of seabed resources with sovereignty over the seabed and sea above. As Commander Larry Parks of the Navy legal staff observed in a *Proceedings* article on the Law of the Sea, "The future conflicts may take the form of a great 'land grab' which would not be in our over-all best interests." President Johnson appeared to adopt this attitude while commissioning a Coast Guard research vessel in 1966. "Under no circumstances must we allow the prospects of rich harvests and mineral wealth to create a new form of colonial competition among the maritime nations," said the President. "We must avoid a race to grab and hold the lands under the high seas. We must ensure that the deep seas and the ocean bottoms are, and remain, the legacy of all humanity."

The possible ignition of a "land grab" suggests the danger in applying a narrow economic or military perspective to the development of undersea technology. Peril at the international level is paralleled on the national level. It would be ironic if Russia were to clean up on ocean resources while the U.S. Navy continues to monopolize America's oceanic capabilities. There have been strong indications that this naval monopoly can retard the full development of these capabilities. The President's advisory Panel on Oceanography criticized technical progress in undersea research programs administered by the Navy and declared, "If the Navy does not adequately pursue programs recommended in this report, program responsibilities for Man in the Sea and undersea technology should be shifted to a civilian agency." The National Council on Marine Resources may find civilian control necessary to reap the full economic and social benefits of such programs. In resisting such a shift, the Navy might resort to parochial slogans of national hypersecurity, or it may practice the attitude expressed by one of its own: "As important as defense-oriented ocean science and technology is, we also recognize the importance of other parts of the national program. . . . Recognizing the equal necessity for these nonmilitary goals is by no means enough; we must offer positive, consequential assistance in addition to moral support," conceded Admiral Odale Waters, Oceanographer of the Navy, in the magazine *Undersea Technology*.

The danger of the military ocean is thus twofold: underestimate the military significance of undersea technology and the ocean can be made to intimidate you; become preoccupied and you can undermine both national and international security. Military capability in the sea thus becomes an exercise in balance. Too little and you encourage enemies on the make; too much and you alienate your friends. England came to realize that striking the flag, impressment, and other projections of national sovereignty were self-defeating and this lesson still has relevance today. The potential value of adhering to the common sea and the shared use concept thus reasserts itself and reaffirms the need for international institutions that can realize this concept in an age of deep-sea exploitation and habitation.

19.

Mare Liberum *Revisited*

THE maintenance of *mare liberum*, however desirable, promises to become progressively more difficult as ocean technology generates more uses and more ambitions. As in the case of the coastal ocean, the relative absence of conflicting activity no longer suffices to ensure a common sea.

Although the temptation to enforce *mare clausum* is strong, most nations seem intent on resisting it, at least in theory. Other heads of state, including Russian leaders, express sentiments similar to President Johnson's: "We must ensure that the deep seas and the ocean bottoms are, and remain, the legacy of all humanity." But these sentiments are useless without the political means to effect them. Grotius, in his later work on international law, grappled with the absence of effective political institutions on the international level. He could only fall back on the hope that nations would always act in good conscience. Yet friendly nations, acting in the very best of conscience, can still fall out over the exploited ocean.

Historic conferences on the law of the sea are helpful. There is considerable agitation in national and international legal circles to modify the open-end clause in the Convention on the Continental Shelf before nations collide in midocean. Yet collisions will be inevitable unless a regional or international agency evolves to administer the deep seabed as a multination resource.

The ocean requires political institutions that can generate accommodation on a continuing, competent, and full-time basis. One institution that may serve is the International Court of Justice which has been successful in resolving problems of navigation rights and measurements of seaward boundaries. Boundary disputes will be on the increase, however, especially in tight seas like the North, the Caribbean and the Mediterranean. If it intends to encourage a rule of law on the common sea, the United States may find it advisable to revoke the Connelly Amendment and accept without reservation the Court's jurisdiction in international law. (Thirty-one nations already do.) As indicated in the case of the fur seals, an international court can have difficulty in assimilating the scientific, economic, and social dimensions of an ocean problem. The countries involved are often their own best authorities here, and a court cannot be relied on to effect Godlike resolutions of problems that require a spirit of mutual concession.

The United Nations, through the Food and Agriculture Association, UNESCO, and the Intergovernmental Oceanographic Commission (IOC), promotes cooperation in ocean exploration and development. Such cooperation can facilitate the critical flow of technical knowledge to developing nations, particularly in regard to fishing. The IOC is presently working to keep proliferating data buoy systems from turning into navigation hazards. It will also sponsor a world conference on ocean pollution, another timely subject.

The UN is destined to play an even greater role in the consideration of ocean management. In 1967, after an address by Malta's Arvid Pardo, the UN formed an Ad Hoc Committee to Study the Peaceful Uses of the Seabed and Ocean Floor Beyond the Limits of Jurisdiction. Opposition to this UN move helped confirm Pardo's expressed fears about the possibility of a land grab and arms race engulfing the seabed. Florida Congressman Paul Rogers declared, "Our national goal in oceanography should be to occupy, with the capacity to defend, out to the mid-Atlantic range." It should be noted that the mid-Atlantic range is not the Atlantic's true middle. It lies decidedly to the east; in fact, it encompasses a possession of Portugal, the Azores. The irritating existence of islands upsets the supposition that a "national lakes" approach necessarily favors the United States. As Francis Christy, Jr. of Resources for the Future notes, the French and the British could lay claim to much of the Atlantic and Pacific seabed because of island ownership.

More restrained critics of UN seabed involvement have urged a go-slow approach. "There was a papal bull that divided the whole New World even before people had a good map of it. I don't know that the UN would be in any better position than the Pope was at the time," observes California Congressman Richard Hanna. Ironically, these calls for caution alternate with proud assertions of the coming feasibility of recovering manganese deposits from the Blake Terrace, a portion of the Atlantic seabed which lies between the Bahama and Bermuda Islands and Florida and which the United States and the United Kingdom may both be claiming.

Contradictions inherent in the national lakes and go-slow approaches have helped foster a more tolerant attitude towards the UN's Ad Hoc Committee. Despite a shortage of time and the wide range of nations represented—from landlocked Austria to sea-grit Ceylon to Russia and the United States—the Committee report announced a "measure of agreement" on the need for an international seabed regime and on restrictions to peaceful purposes. Both Russia and the U.S. have urged the Eighteen-Nation Committee on Disarmament to consider the question of seabed arms control. A UN Permanent Committee on Peaceful Uses of the Seabed now seeks agreement on deep-sea bed boundaries and an international authority to manage it. (The UN has also approved a U.S.-originated proposal for an international decade of ocean exploration.) Such an international authority could set fees on seabed exploitation to help finance development in developing nations and thus share the wealth of the sea. Sen. Clairborne Pell, the sea grant program sponsor, urges this. Clark Eichelberger of the United Nations Association notes that such fees could also help finance the UN. This has led critics to suggest that the UN needs the ocean more than the ocean needs the UN. The question of income use will be a very important factor in consideration of international and UN involvement in ocean affairs.

The regional fish commission may serve as a means or model for a regional ocean commission, a level at which nations might better absorb the complex scientific and political factors at play. Such a commission could formulate antipollution regulations tailored to the currents and biota of a particular region. (Such regulations should prove more readily acceptable than fish quotas.) A regional commission could also recognize exploitative seabed claims and delimit their scope in terms of area covered, time held, and degree of sovereignty exercised.

The regional fish commissions may be able to provide competence without raising the issue of UN financing. As discussed before, they could be expanded to resolve problems raised by mining, pollution, and habitation. They can also function as a means of technical exchange between developed and developing nations. They could forestall military occupation of the deep seabed, regulate the setting aside of the ocean as a bomb range, and help unveil the ocean's tantalizing opacity. Professor William Burke, co-author of *The Public Order of the Oceans,* suggests that Russia and America may choose to patrol jointly all future undersea activities of that incorrigible military mimic, Communist China. (It will be interesting to see how the major powers react when China mimics their setting aside parts of the Pacific for missile and atom bomb tests.) A regional ocean commission could help resolve disputes over nuclear outfalls on an objective basis. (The United States grudgingly withdrew plans to dump low-level nuclear wastes in the Gulf of Mexico after Mexico protested. The nuclear outfall at England's Windscale Works inspired the Dutch to propose UN regulation of such practices.) The less-than-global range of authority could facilitate settlement of local disputes. Recently, European nations jointly agreed on uniform fishery and seabed boundaries tailored to such compact seas as the North, the Baltic and the Mediterranean. Regional ocean commissions could cooperate with one another in solving mutual problems, perhaps in a federation of commissions under United Nations auspices.

California's governor, Ronald Reagan, has already proposed a Pacific Basin Community to develop the Pacific. Yet, if such bodies are to become the pattern of the future, membership becomes increasingly critical. Coastal nations would obviously qualify, but what of noncoastal nations? An open-end membership could conceivably dilute the very worth of a regional ocean commission, including the ocean resources available. Can communist and noncommunist nations cooperate in common ocean areas? The question of membership would not be so crucial in a United Nations Marine Resources Agency, with its all-inclusive character.

The International Court, the United Nations, and the regional fish commissions all offer opportunities for fashioning appropriate instruments of ocean government. The challenging task of examining and exploiting these opportunities remains. The historic struggle over the oceans absorbed the energies of nations, required the attention of their leading intellects, and still continued to flare for more than two centuries. The universal nature of the high seas finally mitigated against exclusive use and compelled nations to seek accommodation or face the specter of friction, depletion, and fragmented effort. Modern technology does not allow such leisured contemplation. In time this technology may de-ice the Arctic Ocean, instantly breach Central America with another canal, and deflect hurricanes with shattering consequences thousands of miles away. Nor can world powers afford to indulge in occasional war. Perfunctory allegiance to freedom of the seas, common property, and shared use will do little to speed the task of developing institutions appropriate to these slogans. The task is formidable, even for nations of good will. Yet there is no reason that a bountiful and rewarding *mare liberum* cannot survive save for the unwillingness of nations to practice what their leaders preach.

Perhaps here will lie the greatest value of the exploited ocean—not in its ability to feed people, to enrich corporations, or to fascinate underwater tourists, but to encourage nations to regard one another as partners in world progress. Should ocean exploitation narrow down to a fierce technological race between Russia and the United States? Should this exploitation only enrich the world's elite—those of us who are already well fed and well clothed—while the world's majority remains hungry, poorly clothed, and increasingly desperate? What will be the more critical achievement, a nuclear storage depot in a deep-sea trench or a fish protein plant in Asia run by Asians tutored in the vision and the technology to satisfy their continent's hunger. If the choices posed seem entirely too stark, it must be remembered that the potential of ocean technology makes them so. The ocean can help alter the world for the better but not if nations regard it as good prize and each other as competitors to be bested or cripples to be ignored.

Epilogue—
To Leave a Clean Wake

THE ultimate challenge of the exploited ocean is clear. It is political. What is "conquered" by technology must be governed, and in this respect an ocean subjected is no different from a nation subdued. This will be true of the coastal ocean and the high seas. The incentives to rational ocean government and use are considerable. So are the obstacles: the passions of exploitation, the abuses of one-eyed technology, the tensions of the cold war, the nagging distrust between poor nations and rich, and, not least of all, human carelessness.

Yet one thing stands on the side of protected and peaceful oceans—our enduring and universal affection for them, as reflected in the works of Byron, Cicero, Winslow Homer, Grotius, Burnham, Conrad, and the millions who walk daily in the hem of the sea. This affection and appreciation has never really been tested for its true depth and strength. Only recently have the oceans really needed man's care. Perhaps this abiding affection will help ensure that the salmon will run in the Columbia, that the whales will spy hop in Scammon Lagoon, that skindivers will glide through sea forests, that the Eastern Tropical Pacific will feed many people, and that the seas will be open to all who respect their nature. The oceans are rapidly becoming ours. Soon they will belong to us, to do with what we will. It will behoove us now and then to read Byron, view Homer, and listen to Debussy. Their oceans should not be forgotten.

Suggested References

A list of sources I found particularly valuable.

BEACHES

American Society of Civil Engineers. *Proceedings of Specialty Conference on Coastal Engineering* (Santa Barbara, 1965). New York: American Society of Civil Engineers, 345 E. 47th St.

Bascom, Willard. *Waves and Beaches*. Garden City, New York: Anchor Books, 1964.

Calif. State Supreme Court. "Miramar Co. v. Santa Barbara," 1943, 23 C. 2d 170.

Council on Wave Research. *Proceedings* Annual conferences on coastal engineering, 1950 on. Richmond, California: Engineering Field Station, University of California.

King, Cuchlaine. *Beaches and Coasts*. London: Edward Arnold, 1959.

U.S. Army Coastal Engineering Research Center. *Land Against The Sea*. Edited by A. C. Rayner. Washington, D.C.: U.S. Army Coastal Engineering Research Center, 1964. (The Center also has technical studies relating to specific problems and locales of beach erosion.)

CULTURE AND FOLKLORE

Byron, George Gordon. *Selected Poetry of Lord Byron*. Edited, with introduction, by Leslie Marchand. New York: Modern Library, 1951.

Gardner, Albert Ten Eyck. *Winslow Homer*. New York, Bramhall House, 1961. (This biographical and critical survey contains thirty-six beautiful color plates and about two hundred black-and-white reproductions.)

Lanier, Sidney. *Centennial Edition of the Works of Sidney Lanier*, Volumes I and VI. Baltimore: Johns Hopkins, 1945.

Malinowski, Bronislaw. *Argonauts of the Western Pacific*. London: Routledge, 1932.

Marchand, Leslie. *Byron*, Three Volumes. New York: Knopf, 1957.

Shay, Frank. *A Sailor's Treasury*. New York: Norton, 1951.

Starke, Aubrey Harrison. *Sidney Lanier*. New York: Russell and Russell, 1964 (c. 1933).

von Groschwitz, Gustave. *The Seashore: Paintings of the 19th and 20th Centuries*. Catalogue of exhibition in 1965. Pittsburgh: Carnegie Institute Museum of Art.

CURRENT EVENT PERIODICALS (emphasis on technology)

Fish Boat. H. L. Peace Publications, 624 Gravier St., New Orleans, La. Monthly.

Naval Research Reviews. Office of Naval Research, Washington, D.C. Monthly.

Oceans—Oceans Publishers, 7075A Mission Gorge Rd., San Diego, Ca. 92120. (General rather than technical.) Monthly.

Sea Frontiers. International Oceanographic Foundation, Institute of Marine Sciences, University of Miami, 1 Rickenbacker Causeway, Miami, Florida. Bimonthly.

Technology Week. American Aviation Publications, 1001 Vermont Ave., Washington, D.C. 20005. Weekly.

Undersea Technology. Compass Publications, 617 Lynn Building, 1111 N. 19th Street, Arlington, Va. 22209. Monthly.

U.S. Naval Institute Proceedings. Annapolis, Maryland 21402. Monthly.

Underwater Naturalist. American Littoral Society, Sandy Hook Marine Laboratory, Highlands, N.J. Quarterly.

FISH AND FISH CONSERVATION (Anadromous, Estuarine and Pelagic)

Bureau of Commercial Fisheries. The Bureau's research branch at La Jolla, California, has helpful reports by Hester, Johnson, Broadhead, Green, McNeely, and Howard on the various aspects of the tuna fishery. United States Bureau of Commercial Fisheries. Biological Laboratory, San Diego, California 92106.

Carlisle, John, Jr., Charles Turner, and Earl Ebert. "Artificial Habitat in the Marine Environment," Fish Bulletin 124, California. Department of Fish and Game. Sacramento, California: Resources Agency of California, 1964.

Cooley, Richard. *Politics and Conservation,* The Decline of the Alaska Salmon. New York: Harper and Row, 1963.

Curtis, Brian. *The Life Story of Fish.* New York: Dover, 1961 (c. 1949).

Hasler, Arthur, and James Larsen. "The Homing Salmon," *Scientific American,* August 1955.

Inter-American Tropical Tuna Commission. The commission has an extensive bibliography of reports and papers by Commission scientists, including Kask, Schaefer, and Klawe, on the Eastern Tropical Pacific. IATTC, c/o Scripps Institution of Oceanography, La Jolla, California 92037.

Johnston, D. *International Law of Fisheries.* New Haven: Yale, 1965.

Masch, Frank. "Shell Dredging—A Factor in Estuarine Sedimentation," Proceedings of Speciality Conference on Coastal Engineering (1965). New York: American Society of Civil Engineers.

Odum, Eugene. "The Role of Tidal Marshes in Estuarine Produc-
tion," New York State *Conservationist,* June–July 1961.
Thompson, Seton. "What Is Happening to Our Estuaries?" Trans-
actions 26th North American Wildlife and Natural Resources'
Conference, 1960.
Tomasevich, Joso. *International Agreements on Conservation of
Marine Resources.* Palo Alto, California: Stanford, 1943.
U.S. Congress, House, Committee on Merchant Marine and
Fisheries. *Anadromous Fish—1965, Hearings.* 89th Cong., 1st
Sess., 1965.
Ibid. Miscellaneous Fisheries Legislation, Hearings (Fish and
Wildlife Coordination Act). 89th Cong., 2nd Sess., 1966.
U.S. Department of the Interior. "Columbia River Fishery Pro-
gram," Circular 192 (1964), Fish and Wildlife Service. Wash-
ington: U.S. Government Printing Office.
Warner, Kendall. "Aroostook River Salmon Restoration," Fishery
Research Bulletin No. 4, 1956. Maine Department of Inland
Fisheries and Game, Augusta, Maine. (This department also
has publications on other aspects of the salmon restoration pro-
gram.)

GRAY WHALE

Gilmore, R. M. "Census of the California Gray Whale," U.S. Fish
and Wildlife Service, Special Scientific Report, Fisheries No.
342, 1960.
Ibid. The Story of the Gray Whale. San Diego: By author, 1958.
Fowler, Gene. *Good Night, Sweet Prince.* London: World Distribu-
tors, 1962 (reprint).
Hubbs, Carl. "Natural History of the Gray Whale," XVth Inter-
national Congress of Zoology, *Proceedings,* July 1958.
Mineral Trade Notes "Salt Industry of Exportadora de Sal, S.A.,"
61, No. 1, 39–40, July 1965 (Publication of U.S. Bureau of
Mines).
Postma, H. "Water Circulation and Suspended Matter in Baja
California Lagoons." *Netherlands Journal of Sea Research,* 2,
4. 566–604, 1965.
Scammon, Charles. *The Marine Mammals of the North-Western
Coast of North America.* San Francisco: John H. Carmany Co.,
1874.
Ibid. Collection of his papers, Bancroft Library, University of
California at Berkeley.
Slijper, E. J. *Whales.* New York: Basic Books, 1962.
Walker, Theodore. *Whale Primer,* with special attention to the
California gray whale. San Diego: Cabrillo Historical Associa-
tion, 1962.
White, Paul Dudley. "Hunting the Heartbeat of the Gray Whale,"
National Geographic Magazine, July 1956.

KELP

California State Water Quality Control Board. "An Investigation of the Effects of Discharged Waters on Kelp," Publication No. 26, 1964, State Water Quality Control Board. Sacramento, California: Office of State Printing.

Institute of Marine Resources. "Kelp Habitat Improvement Project," Quarterly Progress Reports, 1957–1963. La Jolla, California: University of California.

Keck Laboratory of Environmental Health Engineering. "Kelp Habitat Improvement Project," Annual Reports, 1964 on. Pasadena, California: California Institute of Technology.

North, Wheeler. *Biology of the California Kelp Beds.* S-H Service Agency, 31 E. 10th Street, New York, N.Y. 10003, 1968.

Scofield, W. L. "History of Kelp Harvesting in California," *California Fish and Game*, July 1959.

LAW OF THE SEA

Corbett, P. E. *Law and Society in the Relations of States.* New York: Harcourt, Brace and Co., 1951.

Eichelberger, Clark. "The Promise of the Seas' Bounty," *Saturday Review*, June 18, 1966.

Fulton, Thomas, *Sovereignty of the Sea.* Edinburgh: Blackwood, 1911.

Grotius, Hugo. *The Law of Prize and Booty.* Oxford: Clarendon Press, 1950. (*Mare Liberum* forms the twelfth chapter of this book.)

Jessup, Philip. *A Modern Law of Nations.* New York: Macmillan, 1948.

Knight, W. S. M. *The Life and Works of Hugo Grotius.* London: Sweet and Maxwell, 1932.

McDougal, Myres, and William Burke. *Public Order of the Oceans.* New Haven: Yale, 1962.

Reiff, Henry. *The United States and the Treaty Law of the Sea.* Minneapolis: University of Minnesota, 1959.

U.S. Congress, House, Committee on Merchant Marine and Fisheries. "Fishing in U.S. Territorial Waters, Hearings," 88th Cong., 2nd Sess., 1964.

Ibid. "Miscellaneous Fisheries Legislation, Hearings" (fishing rights), 89th Cong., 2nd Sess., 1966.

MARINE DEVELOPMENT AND MANAGEMENT

California State Legislature, Assembly, Interim Committee on Natural Resources. "Filling San Francisco Bay, Hearings," 1963.

California State Legislature, Assembly, Interim Committee on Water. "Pollution of San Francisco Bay, Hearings," 1963.

Institute of Marine Resources. *California: Uses of the Ocean.* La Jolla, Calif.: University of California, 1966.

Interagency Committee on Oceanography. "National Oceanographic Program—1967," ICO Pamphlet Number 24. Washington: U.S. Government Printing Office.

Ibid. "Oceanography: The Ten Years Ahead," ICO Pamphlet Number 10, 1963. Washington: U.S. Government Printing Office.

Moore, Charles. Daniel H. Burnham, 2 vols. Boston: Houghton-Mifflin, 1921.

National Academy of Sciences. "Economic Benefits from Oceanographic Research," Publication 1228, NAS—Committee on Oceanography, 1964. Washington: National Academy of Sciences.

President's Advisory Panel on Oceanography. Effective Uses of the Sea. Washington: U.S. Government Printing Office, 1966.

San Francisco Bay Conservation and Development Commission. San Francisco Bay Plan and Supplement. Sacramento: California Office of State Printing, 1968.

Scott, Mel. The Future of San Francisco Bay. Berkeley: Institute of Governmental Studies, University of California, 1963.

Terry, Richard (editor). Ocean Engineering, 6 vols. Report compiled and published by North American Aviation Corporation, 1964.

U.S. Congress, House, Committee on Merchant Marine and Fisheries. "National Oceanographic Program Legislation, Hearings," 89th Cong., 1st Sess., 1965.

U.S. Congress, Senate, Committee on Labor and Public Welfare. "Hearings before the Special Subcommittee on Sea Grant Colleges," 89th Cong., 2nd Sess., 1966. (Includes Proceedings, National Conference on the Concept of a Sea Grant University, 1965.)

Wisconsin State Department of Resource Development. "Waterfront Renewal," report for the U.S. Department of Housing and Urban Development. Washington: U.S. Government Printing Office, 1966.

MILITARY OCEAN

Ageton, Arthur, R. Adm. The Naval Officer's Guide, 6th Edition. Annapolis: U.S. Naval Institute, 1964.

Baar, James, and William Howard. Polaris! New York: Harcourt, Brace, 1960.

Baldwin, Hanson. The New Navy. New York: Dutton, 1964.

Brodie, Bernard. A Guide to Naval Strategy. Princeton, N. J.: Princeton, 1943.

Garthoff, Raymond. Soviet Military Doctrine. Glencoe: The Free Press, 1953.

Lewis, Michael. The Navy of Britain. London: George Allen, 1948.

Lloyd, Christopher. Ships and Seamen. New York: World, 1961.

Polmar, Norman. *Atomic Submarines*. Princeton: Van Nostrand, 1963.

Saunders, M. G. Editor, *The Soviet Navy*. London: Weidenfeld and Nicolson, 1958.

POLLUTION

Butler, Philip, and Paul Springer. "Pesticides—A New Factor in Coastal Environments," Transactions, 28th North American Wildlife and Natural Resources Conference, 1963.

Cowen, Robert. *Frontiers of the Sea*. New York: Doubleday, 1960.

Dunster, H. J. "Nuclear Power and the Sea," Proceedings, California Governor's Conference on "California and the World Ocean," 1964.

Hedgpeth, Joel. *Introduction to Seashore Life of the San Francisco Bay Region and the Coast of Northern California*. Berkeley: University of California, 1962.

Kurland, Leonard, Stanley Fard and Howard Siedler. "Minamata Disease," *World Neurology*, November, 1960.

Malley, Nuri, and Carl Lorenzen. "Automated Fluorometric Measurement of Chlorophyll in the Ocean as an Indicator for Oil Pollution Effect on Fisheries," Paper submitted before Offshore Exploration Conference, Long Beach, Calif., 1966.

Revelle, Roger, and Milner Schaefer. "General Considerations Concerning the Ocean as a Receptacle for Artificially Radioactive Materials," Contribution from the Scripps Institution of Oceanography, New Series, No. 901, 1957.

Schaefer, Milner. "Some Fundamental Aspects of Marine Ecology in Relation to Radioactive Wastes," 1960 Contribution from the Scripps Institution of Oceanography, New Series.

Uchida, Makio. "Biochemical Studies on Minamata Disease," *Kumamoto Medical Journal* (Japan), 14, No. 4, 1961, and 15, No. 3–4, 1962.

U.S. Department of Interior. "The Effects of Pesticides on Fish and Wildlife," Circular 226, Fish and Wildlife Service, 1965.

ZoBell, Claude. "The Occurrence, Effects, and Fate of Oil Polluting the Sea," Proceedings, International Conference on Water Pollution Research, 1962. London: Pergamon Press.

RED TIDE (Discolored Water)

Hunter, S. H., and John McLaughlin. "Poisonous Tides," *Scientific American*, August 1958.

Ingle, Robert, and John Torpey. "The Red Tide," Educational Series No. 1, Florida Board of Conservation, 1966.

Marvin, Kenneth, and Raphael Proctor, Jr. "Laboratory Evaluation of Red Tide Control Agents," Contribution No. 215, Bureau of Commercial Fisheries Biological Laboratory, Galveston, Tex., 1966.

Stephan, E. C., R. Adm. "Discolored Water," *Science Teacher*, November, 1962.

U.S. Department of the Interior. "Florida Red Tide," Fishery Leaflet 506, Fish and Wildlife Service.

Ibid. "Bureau of Commercial Fisheries Symposium on Red Tide," Special Scientific Report—Fisheries No. 521, Fish and Wildlife Service, 1965.

Wilson, W. B., et al. "The Occurrence of a Ciguatera-like Poison in Oysters, Clams, and Gymnodinium Breve Cultures," *Toxicon*, 1965, 3, 111–123. London: Pergamon Press.

Appendices

Appendix A

Comparative Annual Production, Live Weight of Animals in Pounds per Acre[1]

	Animal	Yield (Average or range)
Sea water, unfertilized:[2]		
Fishponds, Philippines	Milkfish	400–980
Fishponds, France	Gray mullet	300
Fishponds, Java	Milkfish	
Poorest		40
Richest		300
Fishponds, Indonesia	Milkfish	140
	Prawns	46
	Wild fish	23
North Sea, 1922	Fish	21.3
World marine fishery[3]	Do	0.45
Adriatic[4]	Do	4.6
Middle Atlantic Continental Shelf[4]	Do	61.9
Humboldt Current, Peru[6]	Anchovy	300
Chesapeake Bay[5] oyster bottom	Oyster	600
Sea water, fertilized:[2]		
Fishponds, Formosa	Milkfish	1,000
Brackish water, fertilized		
Experimental fish farm, Palestine	Carp	755–7, 970
Commercial ponds, Palestine	Do	356–4, 210
Land:		
Cultivated land	Swine	450
Grassland	Cattle	5–250

[1] Data unless otherwise indicated from C. H. Mortimer and C. F. Hickling, "Fertilizers in Fishponds." Fishery Pub. No. 5, 1957. London: Her Majesty's Stationery Office.

[2] Ponds constructed so that sea water can enter through gates. Gates can be closed to contain fish.

[3] C. L. Cutting. Economic Aspects of utilization of fish. Biochemical Society Symposium No. 6. Biochemical Society. Cambridge, England.

[4] Range of values for selected ocean areas listed by H. W. Graham and R. L. Edwards. 1961. Fish in nutrition.

[5] J. L. McHugh. In press. In *Symposium on Estuaries.* American Association for Advancement of Science.

[6] M. B. Schaefer. 1965. Transactions American Fisheries Society. Vol. 94, pp. 123, 128.

(Table reproduced from "Effective Use of the Sea," report by President's Advisory Panel on Oceanography.)

Appendix B

America's Anadromous Nurseries

West Coast Streams and Species

A. CALIFORNIA

Chinook salmon, steelhead, shad, striped bass, sturgeon
1. Sacramento and San Joaquin Rivers and tributaries, such as Feather River, Yuba River, Clear Creek, Cottonwood Creek, Stony Creek, American River, Mokelumne River, and Consumnes River.
2. Russian River.
3. Garcia River.
4. Gualala River.
5. Navarro River.
6. Noyo River.
7. Eel River.
8. Van Duzen River.
9. Mad River.
10. Klamath River.
11. Smith River.
12. Trinity River.

B. OREGON

Steelhead, silver salmon, chinook salmon, chum salmon, shad, striped bass, sea run cutthroat trout, white sturgeon
1. Rogue River.
2. Alsea River.
3. Coquille River.
4. Nehalem River.
5. Necanicum River.
6. Siletz River.
7. Nestucca River.
8. Trask.
9. Umpqua.
10. Wilson.
11. Coos.

C. WASHINGTON

Steelhead, chinook salmon, silver salmon, sea run cutthroat trout, white sturgeon
1. Green.

2. Skagit.
3. Hoh.
4. Queets.
5. Samish.
6. Snohomish.
7. Nisqually.
8. Skokomish.
9. Stillaquamish.
10. Naselle.
11. Deschutes
12. Humptulips.
   (Also Soos, Nemah, Bear, Elwha, Willapa, Puyallup, Duwamish, Quillayute, Dungeness.)

D. ALASKA

All five species of Pacific salmon (chinook, silver, chum, pink, and sockeye) and steelhead

1. Naknek.
2. Yukon.
3. Kuskokwim.
4. Kvichak.
5. Copper (Iliamna Lake).
6. Karluk.
7. Stikine.
8. Copper River (Prince William Sound).
9. Wood.
10. Nushagak.
11. Igushik.
12. Nuyakuk.
13. Hunter Creek, S.E.
14. Klakas Creek, S.E.
15. Klawak Creek, S.E.
16. Shaheen Creek, S.E.
17. Sunny Creek, S.E.
18. Tom Creek, S.E.

EAST COAST

A. MAINE

1. Penobscot	Atlantic salmon.
2. Kennebec	Atlantic salmon, shad.
3. Narraguagus	Atlantic salmon.
4. St. Croix	Do.
5. Machias	Do.
6. Dennys	Do.
7. Saco	Do.
8. Little Falls Stream	Do.

9. Chandler ....   Do.
10. Ducktrap ....   Do.
11. Tunk ....   Do.
12. Sheepscot ....   Do.

B. NEW YORK AND NEW JERSEY

Hudson ....   Shad, striped bass.

C. CONNECTICUT

Connecticut ....   Shad, striped bass.

D. MARYLAND

1. Susquehanna ....   Shad.
2. Potomac ....   Do.

E. DELAWARE

Delaware ....   Striped bass, shad.

F. MASSACHUSETTS

Merrimac ....   Striped bass, shad.

G. VIRGINIA

1. Potomac ....   Shad, striped bass, alewives, herring.
2. James ....   Do.
3. York ....   Do.
4. Rappahannock ....   Shad.
5. Anacostia ....   Do.

H. NORTH CAROLINA

1. Neuse ....   Striped bass, herring, shad,
2. Cape Fear ....   Do.
3. Roanoke ....   Do.
4. Tar ....   Do.
5. Pee Dee ....   Do.
6. White Oak ....   Do.
7. Little River ....   Do.
8. Scuppernong ....   Do.
9. Chowan ....   Do.

I. SOUTH CAROLINA

1. Savannah ....   Striped bass, shad.
2. Cooper ....   Striped bass, herring, sturgeon.
3. Edisto ....   Striped bass, shad.
4. Combahee ....   Do.

5. Ashepoo	Do.
6. Santee	Striped bass, herring, shad.
7. Big Pee Dee	Striped bass, shad.
8. Waccamaw	Do.

J. FLORIDA

1. St. Johns	Shad and striped bass.
2. Apalachicola	Striped bass.
3. Indian	Do.

K. GEORGIA

1. Ogeechee	Striped bass.
2. Canoochee	Do.
3. Savannah	Do.
4. Flint	Do.
5. Chattahoochee	Do.
6. Altamaha	Do.

L. ALABAMA

1. Chattahoochee	Striped bass.
2. Tombigbee	Do.

(List prepared by U.S. Fish and Wildlife Service.)

Appendix C

Presidential Ocean Program for Fiscal Year 1968

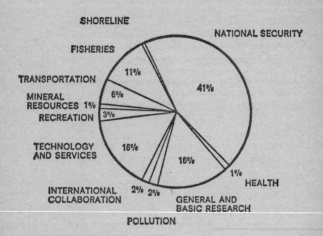

MARINE SCIENCES AND TECHNOLOGY DOLLAR

*LESS THAN 1%

*The marine sciences and technology dollar for fiscal year
1968 is shown in terms of the programs it will support.
Oceanography for national security will require 41% of
the $462.3 million requested.*

From *Technology Week*, March 13, 1967.
Author's Note: The National Sea-Grant College program, discussed
in Chapter 10, is funded at $4 million dollars, or 0.009 per cent of the
total budget.

APPENDIX D

America's Backward Fish Fleet

14,000 DOCUMENTED U.S. FISHING BOATS

38% Have Electric Plants
    62% HAVE NOT

16% Have Hydraulic Winches
    84% HAVE NOT

5% Have Hydraulic Steering
    95% HAVE NOT

8% Have Refrigeration
    92% HAVE NOT

31% Have Automatic Pilots
    67% HAVE NOT

23% Have Direction Finders
    77% HAVE NOT

52% Have Radiotelephones
    48% HAVE NOT

—1% Have Salt-Water Evaporators
    +99% HAVE NOT

and 16% have not had their engines overhauled in the last eight years

(From *Fish Boat*, February 1966)

Appendix E

Breadth of Fishery Jurisdiction Claimed by Coast

3 miles	3 to 12 miles	12 miles
*Australia	Cameroon (6)	Albania
China (Formosa)	*Finland (4)	Algeria
Cuba	Greece (6)	Belgium
Ivory Coast	*Haiti	Brazil
Japan	Honduras (6)	Bulgaria
Jordan	Israel (6)	Burma
Kenya	Lebanon (6)	Canada
Liberia	Maldive Island (6)	China
Malaysia	Mexico (9)	(Mainland)
Malta	Yugoslavia (10)	*Colombia
Poland		Cyprus
The Gambia		Dahomey
Trinidad		Denmark
		Ethiopia
		France
		Germany
		Guatemala
		Iceland
		Indonesia

NOTES

1. 23 nations that are members of United Nations have no coast.

2. As of June 1, 1966, Department of State had incomplete information on fishery jurisdiction claims of 8 coastal nations—Congo (Brazzaville, Congo (Léopoldville), Gabon, Kuwait, *Nigeria (3-mile territorial sea, fishery jurisdiction uncertain), Philippines (expansive use of straight base lines, fishery jurisdiction uncertain), Somali Republic, and Yemen.

al Nations, Compiled by U.S. State Dept. in 1966

12 miles		Beyond 12 miles
Iran	Spain	Argentina (200)
Iraq	Sudan	*Cambodia (CS)
Ireland	Sweden	Ceylon (100)
Italy	Syria	Chile (200)
Jamaica	Tanzania	Costa Rica (200)
Libya	Thailand	*Dominican Republic (15)
*Malagasy	Togo	Ecuador (200)
Republic	Turkey	El Salvador (200)
Mauritania	Ukrainian S.S.R.	Ghana (100)
Morocco	U.S.S.R.	Guinea (130)
*Netherlands	United States	India (100)
New Zealand	United Arab	Korea (200)
Norway	Republic	Nicaragua (200)
*Portugal	*United Kingdom	Pakistan (100)
Romania	Uruguay	Panama (200)
Saudi Arabia	*Venezuela	Peru (200)
Senegal	Vietnam	Tunisia (65)
Sierra Leone		
*South Africa		

3. Numbers in parentheses indicate approximate number of miles claimed; "CS" means continental shelf.

4. The nature of the claims of several nations beyond 12 miles is uncertain.

5. "*" indicates nations that have ratified the 1958 Convention on Fishing and Conservation of the Living Resources of the Sea.

APPENDIX F

International Fish Commissions Adhered To by United States

1. International Commission for the Northwest Atlantic Fisheries (est. 1949)
   Members: Canada, Denmark, France, Germany, Iceland, Italy, Norway, Poland, Spain, U.S.S.R., United States, United Kingdom. This commission works with member governments toward achieving maximum productivity of the fisheries of the Northwest Atlantic. Large research programs by member nations are coordinated by various panels of the Commission. Recommendations on regulations are also made by Commission panels. Mesh regulations adopted for two ocean areas resulted in increased yields of haddock.

2. International Atlantic Tuna Commission (1966)
   Nations which drafted the Convention that created the Commission: United Kingdom, Spain, France, Argentina, Canada, Japan, South Korea, Senegal, Brazil, United States, Cuba, Portugal, Congo, South Africa, U.S.S.R., Uruguay, Venezuela. (English, Spanish and French the official languages.)
   This new commission is designed to develop Atlantic tuna resources and recommend any needed regulations to member nations. Designed in part after the Inter-American Tropical Tuna Commission. As many as sixty nations may eventually become a party to this commission.

3. International Commission on Whaling (1948)
   Members: Argentina, Australia, Brazil, Canada, Chile, Denmark, France, Japan, Mexico, Netherlands, New Zealand, Norway, Peru, U.S.S.R., United Kingdom and Northern Ireland, United States and Union of South Africa.
   This commission originated in the International Agreement for the Regulation of Whaling signed in London in 1937. This commission recommends and reviews research programs. It also recommends whaling seasons, fixing areas and whale quotas for some eight whale species. Because of the reluctance of some member nations to heed these recommendations, whaling is now at its lowest ebb.

4. The Great Lakes Fishery Commission (1955)
   Members: Canada, United States.

272

This commission develops research programs into the Great Lakes fish stocks. It can also recommend regulations to the two participating parties. This commission has cooperated with the Bureau of Commercial Fisheries in controlling the sea lamprey. This bloodsucking, eellike parasite nearly destroyed the seven and a half million dollar trout fishing industry in Lakes Huron, Superior, and Michigan. The Bureau now treats some seventy-seven lamprey spawning streams with a chemical substance called lampricide.

5. International North Pacific Fisheries Commission (1952)
   Members: Canada, Japan, United States.
   This commission seeks to conserve fish stocks in the North Pacific Ocean. It provides that member nations abstain from fishing stocks that one or more countries are fully utilizing and have under conservation management. The concept of "abstention" has, in practice, been aimed at Japanese fishing of Pacific salmon stocks. Japan, however, has not always been willing to accept the consequences of abstention. The treaty convention which brought this commission into being is presently being renegotiated.

6. International Pacific Halibut Commission (1924)
   Members: United States, Canada.
   By management of the halibut resources of the North Pacific and the Bering Sea this commission brought the yearly yield from a depleted low of forty-four million pounds in 1931 to a yield of seventy million at present. This conservation accomplishment is dimmed somewhat by the economic picture. With the halibut resources open to all comers in the common-property concept, the fishery becomes a marginal proposition. More than fifty per cent of the halibut fishermen draw some kind of unemployment compensation. This factor does not tend to attract young blood; about twenty-five per cent of the Pacific halibut fishermen are more than sixty years old. Recently the North Pacific Fisheries Commission opened halibut stocks in the Bering Sea to Japanese fishermen. The Japanese soon reduced these stocks to a low level. The two commissions are now trying to get their signals straight.

7. International Pacific Salmon Commission (1937)
   Members United States, Canada.
   In 1913 railroad construction activity accidentally triggered a rock slide that choked off bountiful salmon runs in Canada's Fraser River. This commission was formed to remove salmon barriers, restore the bountiful runs, and regulate the catch. The commission has rebuilt sockeye salmon stocks and is now working to do the same for pink salmon. The Fraser River empties into Washington State's Puget Sound; United States

and Canadian fishermen catch near-equal amounts of the Fraser River run.
8. Inter-American Tropical Tuna Commission (see Chapter 16, p. 183).
9. Pacific Fur Seal Convention (see Chapter 17, p. 196).

Psychotherapy East & West

Alan W. Watts

Eternity is *Now*—and in this major book Alan
Watts explores the ways of liberation developed
by East and West: liberation from repression
of the body and emotions, liberation from the
prison of the ego, liberation from the meaningless routines of consumption and production
that our civilization has imposed on mankind.
By the author of *The Book: On the Taboo
Against Knowing Who You Are.*

A BALLANTINE BOOK   **$.95**

The Politics of
Experience

R. D. Laing

Given the conditions of contemporary civilization how can one claim that the "normal" man is sane?

In this already famous book, a young British psychiatrist attacks the Establishment assumptions about "normality" with a radical and challenging view of the mental sickness built into our society . . .

"He has let us know. He has told us in such a way that we can not disregard it. . . . He speaks to no one but you and me."—Los Angeles Free Press

A BALLANTINE BOOK   *$.95*

Like JORDI/LISA AND DAVID—the deeply moving account of a small boy's successful struggle for identity. . . .

DIBS
IN SEARCH OF SELF

by Virginia M. Axline

Virginia M. Axline, author of *Play Therapy*, is the acknowledged authority on play therapy in the treatment of disturbed children. In *Dibs* she makes the reader a partner in an extraordinarily affecting—because true—situation: the emergence of intelligence and emotion in a five-year-old boy so withdrawn that even his own parents have judged him mentally defective. But Dibs, as it turned out, was a brilliant child, and in this transcript of his treatment, much of it taken from actual tapes, there emerges the personality of a child whom the reader will leave with an enormous sense of affection and admiration. In his spirit and courage, Dibs is as wonderful a child as the young Helen Keller, and his final mastery of emotional communication parallels her physical triumph. *(224 pages, $.75)*